Red Deer in the Highlands

Red Deer in the Highlands

T. H. Clutton-Brock MA, PhD, ScD and S. D. Albon BSc, PhD
Large Animal Research Group
Department of Zoology
Cambridge

With original drawings by Dafila Scott

BSP PROFESSIONAL BOOKS

OXFORD LONDON EDINBURGH

BOSTON MELBOURNE

First published in Great Britain by
BSP Professional Books, 1989

British Library
Cataloguing in Publication Data

Clutton-Brock, T.H.
  Red deer in the Highlands.
  1. Scotland. Highlands. Red deer
  I. Title
  599.73′57

ISBN 0-632-02244-2

BSP Professional Books
A division of Blackwell Scientific
  Publications Ltd
Editorial Offices:
Osney Mead, Oxford OX2 0EL
  (Orders: Tel. 0865 240201)
8 John Street, London WC1N 2ES
23 Ainslie Place, Edinburgh EH3 6AJ
3 Cambridge Center, Suite 208,
  Cambridge, MA 02142, USA
107 Barry Street, Carlton, Victoria 3053,
  Australia

Set by Action Typesetting Limited,
Gloucester
Printed and bound in Great Britain by
MacKays of Chatham PLC, Kent

Contents

Acknowledgements   vi

1   Red Deer in the Highlands   1
    1.1   Introduction   1
    1.2   Habitat and management   7
    1.3   The history and pre-history of red deer   11
    1.4   Red deer in Scotland   13
    1.5   Summary   18

2   Red Deer Populations   23
    2.1   Introduction   23
    2.2   Deer counts and changes in population
          density   23
    2.3   Geographical variation in red deer density   29
    2.4   Culls and culling rates   34
    2.5   Implications for management   37
    2.6   Summary   41

3   Social Behaviour, Reproduction, Growth and
    Survival   45
    3.1   Introduction   45
    3.2   Social behaviour and dispersal   45
    3.3   Reproduction   49
    3.4   Calf survival   55
    3.5   Growth and antler development   57
    3.6   Reproductive performance and age   63
    3.7   The costs of breeding   67
    3.8   Implications for management   70
    3.9   Summary   73

4   Feeding Behaviour and Habitat Use   79
     4.1 Introduction   79
     4.2 Feeding behaviour and appetite   83
     4.3 Diet and habitat use   85
     4.4 Differences in diet and habitat use between stags
          and hinds   93
     4.5 The impact of deer populations on their habitat   94
     4.6 Muirburn and deer   96
     4.7 Supplementary feeding   97
     4.8 Deer, sheep and cattle   99
     4.9 Implications for management   102
     4.10 Summary   105

5   Population Density, Reproduction and Survival   113
     5.1 Introduction   113
     5.2 Population density and fecundity   115
     5.3 Population density and mortality   118
     5.4 Population density and growth   124
     5.5 Population density and dispersal   124
     5.6 Implications for management   125
     5.7 Summary   129

6   Weather and Red Deer Populations   133
     6.1 Introduction   133
     6.2 Climate, body weight and condition   135
     6.3 Climate and fecundity   139
     6.4 Climate, conception and calving dates   140
     6.5 Climate and birth weight   142
     6.6 Climate and calf mortality in summer   142
     6.7 Climate and juvenile mortality in winter   144
     6.8 Climate and adult mortality   147
     6.9 Climate and differences in reproductive
          performance between cohorts   149
     6.10 Implications for management   152
     6.11 Summary   154

7   Red Deer in Commercial Forests   159
     7.1 Introduction   159
     7.2 Population density   159
     7.3 Growth and reproductive performance   161
     7.4 Habitat preferences and feeding   164

7.5 Impact on forests   167
7.6 Interactions with roe and sika deer   172
7.7 Implications for management   174
7.8 Summary   178

8   Red Deer Research and Management   185
8.1 Introduction   185
8.2 Population dynamics of red deer in the Highlands   185
8.3 Management and population dynamics   192
8.4 Management decisions   200
8.5 Summary   206

Appendices:

Appendix 1: The Accuracy of Deer Counts   210
Appendix 2: Estimating Variation in Deer Density: the
   Block-year Model   216
Appendix 3: Temporal Variation in Deer Density in the
   Highlands   227
Appendix 4: The Correlates of Spatial Variation in Deer
   Density   233
Appendix 5: Deer Densities in the Red Deer
   Commission's Counting Blocks   248

Subject Index   250
Author Index   258

Acknowledgements

We are grateful to the Highlands and Islands Development Board, The Rannoch Trust, the Red Deer Commission and the United Nations Environmental Programme for funding our research into variation in population density of red deer in Scotland and to the Red Deer Commission for providing census data and for their co-operation throughout this part of the project. The work could not have been carried out without their support. Research on Rhum is funded by the Natural Environment Research Council and the Science and Engineering Research Council. We are also grateful to the owners and factors of the deer forests that gave permission for us to have access to the statistics for their estates; to Neil Sutherland and Malcolm Pearson for encouragement; to Brian Mitchell, Brian Staines, Fred Last, David Ball and Robert Bunce of the Institute of Terrestrial Ecology and to Phillip Ratcliffe of the Forestry Commission and Peter Martin of the Department of Agriculture and Fisheries for Scotland for advice, assistance or access to unpublished information; to Lord Dulverton, Hugh Oliver-Bellasis, Mark Boyce, Hugh Rose, Adam Watson, Robert Moss, Brian Staines, Nigel Leader-Williams, and the Red Deer Commission for critical comments on the manuscript; and finally to our colleagues on Rhum and at Cambridge, including Fiona Guinness, Robin Anderson, Iain Gordon, Glenn Iason, Callan Duck, Martin Major, David Green and Richard Clarke, Robin Gill, Jeremy John, Andrew Balmford, Sarah Blakeman, Colleen Burgoyne, Stephen Jacquest, Robert Fryer and Richard Morris. We are especially grateful to Jacqueline Hodkinson for deciphering and typing the manuscript and to Ian Stephenson for compiling the index.

This book represents our own assessment of existing knowledge of red deer and does not necessarily reflect the views of the Red Deer Commission or any other body.

For permission to reproduce published figures, we are grateful to the following: G.K. Whitehead and Constable (Figure 1.3); the Red

Deer Commission (Figure 2.1); the University of Chicago Press (Figures 3.1, 3.10, 3.11, 4.4, 4.7, 4.8, 5.6, 5.10); Brian Mitchell and the Zoological Society of London (Figures 3.3, 3.5, 3.13, 7.3); *Scientific American* (Figure 3.4); V.P.W. Lowe and Blackwell Scientific Publications Ltd (Figures 3.6, 3.7); G. Lincoln and the British Deer Society (Figure 3.9); the British Ecological Society (Figures 3.11, 5.3, 5.4, 5.5, 5.8, 5.9, 6.19, 6.20); the American Society of Naturalists (Figure 3.12); R.N.B. Kay (Figure 4.5); B. Mitchell and the Natural Environment Research Council (Figure 4.6); the Zoological Society of London (Figures 4.9, 6.8, 6.17); S.A. Grant and the British Ecological Society (Figure 4.10); G.R. Miller and the British Ecological Society (Figure 4.11); B.C. Osborne and the British Ecological Society (Figure 4.12); I.R. Colquhoun (Figure 4.13); the Royal Society of Edinburgh (Figures 5.2, 5.11); Macmillans Publishers (Figure 5.7, 8.2); Adam Watson and the British Ecological Society (Figures 6.1, 6.9, 6.12, 6.15); the *Journal of Wild Life Management* (Figure 6.3); P.R. Ratcliffe and *Acta Zoologica Fennica* (Figure 7.2); P.R. Ratcliffe (Figure 7.4); B.W. Staines and the Royal Society of Edinburgh (Figure 7.5); P.R. Ratcliffe and the Mammal Society of Great Britain (Figure 7.8); G. Caughley (Figure 8.9).

We are also grateful to Lea MacNally, Brian Mitchell, Brian Staines and Fiona Guinness for permission to use photographs; to Dafila Scott for the illustrations at the beginning of each chapter; and to Guinness P.L.C. for their kind permission to reproduce Landseer's *Monarch of the Glen*.

T.H. Clutton-Brock
S.D. Albon

1 Red Deer in the Highlands

1.1 INTRODUCTION

Over three-quarters of the Scottish Highlands are used by red deer (*Cervus elaphus*), an area of some 30,000 square kilometres of bare, open hills, interspersed with occasional woodlands and plantations, which currently supports some 300,000 animals. Partly because of their open habitat and partly because of their economic significance, the ecology of Scottish red deer has been more extensively studied than that of any other deer population of a similar size in the world[1-3].

The aim of this book is to synthesize the results of research on the ecology of Scottish red deer so that they may be used to guide decisions about deer management. Since the factors affecting deer numbers and performance vary locally, as well as between different parts of the Highlands, universal prescriptions for management are unlikely to be useful. Instead, we believe that it is important that managers should understand the likely consequences of environmental changes for red deer. Combined with local knowledge and supplemented by trial and error, an understanding of the ecology of Highland deer provides the most likely basis for successful management. In the seven chapters that follow we review the areas of research that have the most direct bearing on management. Chapter 2 describes variation in red deer numbers on the open hill; Chapter 3, reproduction and growth; Chapter 4, feeding ecology and habitat use; and Chapters 5 and 6, the effects of population density and weather on reproduction and survival. In Chapter 7 we review the more limited information on red deer living in woodland and forestry plantations. Finally, in Chapter 8 we discuss the principal findings of research on Highland red deer and explore some of their implications for management.

Throughout this book, we use the term 'Highlands' in its least restrictive sense to refer to the uplands of mainland Scotland north of the Central Valley, including the Hebridean Islands (see Figure 1.1). Only a part of this area falls within the administrative area of the Highland Region (see Figure 2.1). Apart from commercial forestry plantations (see Chapter 7) and the sad remnants of the great Scots pine forest that once covered most of the Highlands, trees are usually sparse and most of the area is covered by grasses, sedges and heather[2], though individual stalking estates retain the name of deer 'forests'. The land is largely unfenced, but most of it is privately owned in holdings of 200 square kilometres or more.

Research on Highland red deer also has implications for studies of many other large mammals. One consistent theme running through much of the work is the marginal nature of most Highland habitats. Red deer evolved as a low-ground species, occupying heaths, woodland and forest margins. The open hills of the Highlands offer little shelter and both the quality and abundance of food is impoverished. As a result, the body size of deer living on the open hill is substantially lower than that of deer living in forestry plantations or on deer farms (see Chapter 7). In addition, we might expect changes in climate to exert a strong influence on reproduction and survival. Like red deer, many other large mammals persist only in marginal environments and the studies of red deer may help to indicate the likely effects of density-independent factors in other populations.

A second recurrent theme is the extent to which behaviour, ecology and population dynamics vary between the sexes. Stags and hinds differ in growth rates, nutritional requirements, habitat use, dispersal and social behaviour, as well as in their susceptibility to malnutrition and hard weather. Many of these differences can be attributed to the contrasting selection pressures that have operated on the two sexes: while hinds are well adapted to the efficient conversion of energy into offspring, stags have been selected to maximize their ability to acquire mates in the autumn, sacrificing economy for characteristics that enable them to fight successfully[3]. Their elaborate weaponry, larger size and higher activity levels all have substantial costs and they are consequently more strongly affected by harsh weather or food shortage. As a result, it is usually preferable to regard hind and stag populations as two separate entities and to avoid assuming that they will respond in a similar fashion to changes in environment or management.

The studies that we draw on fall into three main categories. First, there are the Red Deer Commission's counts which provide a unique description of variation in population density and management throughout the length and breadth of the Highlands since 1961. Though the Commission's counts have been published in their annual reports[4] no previous attempt has been made to standardize estimates of population density within particular time frames or to explore their causes (see Chapter 2).

Second, there are studies of the ecology of particular populations. Seventeen different populations have now been investigated to some extent (see Figure 1.1) though much of our knowledge of red deer

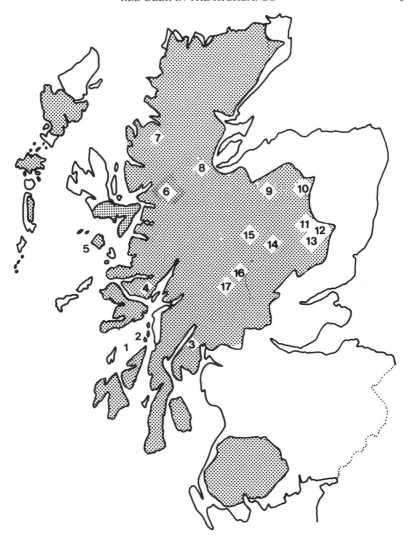

Figure 1.1 Highland deer populations whose ecology has been studied:
(1) Jura[5]; (2) Scarba[6]; (3) Glen Branter[7-9]; (4) Morvern[10]; (5) Rhum[3,11,12,13];
(6) South Ross[14]; (7) Dundonnell[1]; (8) Glen Goibhre[15]; (9) Corndavon[16,17];
(10) Glen Fiddich[18]; (11) Glen Tanar[19]; (12) Glen Dye[20,21]; (13) Invermark[18,22];
(14) Glen Lui[19]; (15) Glenfeshie[2,22,24]; (16) Killin[25]; (17) Ben Lawers[26].

ecology is based on studies carried out at only two sites and its
generality has still to be established. Fortunately, the two areas in
which red deer have been most extensively studied (Glenfeshie in the
Central Highlands and the Island of Rhum on the west coast) differ
in climate and consequently provide a useful basis for comparison.

Plate 1.1 Glenfeshie in the spring. Scots pine and juniper are still relatively abundant on the lower ground. (Photograph: Brian Mitchell.)

Plate 1.2 Kilmory Glen, Rhum. Hill slopes are covered by sparse heather, deer sedge and purple moor grass, the bed of the Glen by grassland communities dominated by bents and fescues with a wide variety of herbs. (Photograph: Tim Clutton-Brock.)

Plate 1.3   Deeside in spring. Compared to most other areas of the Highlands, Deeside and its neighbouring glens are fertile and well wooded. (Photograph: Brian Mitchell.)

Glenfeshie is high with much of its ground over 500 metres, extensive heather cover and a cold, comparatively dry climate (Plate 1.1). In contrast, much of Rhum (Plate 1.2) is low lying and the ground is broken, heather cover is patchy and the climate is mild and wet, with little snow cover in most years (see Chapter 6). Both areas carry around 13 deer per square kilometre and hinds and stags are culled annually. However, in one part of Rhum (the North Block, an area of around 12 square kilometres) culling was ceased in 1972 and population density was allowed to increase naturally from 15 to 24 deer per square kilometre by 1983 (see Chapter 5). Throughout these years, all deer that regularly used the North Block could be recognized individually from ear tags or natural characteristics and much of the most detailed information on red deer is derived from studies in this area[3]. When comparing results from this area with other studies it is important to remember that population density in the North Block of Rhum was higher than is usual in the Highlands.

Plate 1.4   Glen Dye, Eastern Highlands – a landscape dominated by heather. (Photograph: Brian Staines.)

Plate 1.5   Scarba from Luing. This island forest supported a very high density of deer [6]. (Photograph: Brian Mitchell.)

The other areas where the demography of Highland red deer populations has been investigated in detail include Glen Fiddich, Invermark, Glen Lui and Glen Tannar (Plate 1.3) and Glen Dye (Plate 1.4) in the eastern Highlands, Wester Ross and South Ross in western Scotland and the islands of Jura and Scarba (Plate 1.5). Highland deer populations living in forestry plantations have also been studied in Glen Cripesdale, and Glen Branter.

Third, studies in research institutes and on deer farms (mostly at the Rowett Research Institute outside Aberdeen and at the Glensaugh deer farm in the eastern Highlands) have investigated the physiology of growth, reproduction and digestion[27-29]. The results of these studies provide invaluable insights into the physiological processes underlying differences between populations on the open hill but it is important to remember that animals are maintained at a level of nutrition far above that of natural populations.

1.2   HABITAT AND MANAGEMENT

Highland red deer share their habitat with mountain hares (*Lepus timidus*) and red grouse (*Lagopus lagopus scoticus*) which are abundant in areas where heather (*Calluna vulgaris*) is dominant but are sparsely distributed over the rest of the deer range. Of greater importance to the deer are the numbers of sheep using the hills. The deer ground of the Highlands supports over 3 million hill sheep (mostly Scottish Blackfaces) at densities ranging from less than 10 to over 200 per square kilometre (see Figure 1.2). In the south and west where the grasslands provide food throughout the year, sheep are usually wintered on the hill while in the north and east where snow accumulation is greater they are more commonly removed to low ground at the onset of winter.

Red deer play an important role in the economy of the Highlands[30,31]. Most of the larger estates still employ one or more stalkers whose job it is to guide the owner, his guests or, most frequently, his shooting tenants on the hill, to decide which stags should be shot, to retrieve the carcase and to prepare it for sale (Plate 1.6). Where stalking is leased to tenants, the lease often specifies the area of the estate that can be stalked and the number of stags that can be killed. The estate provides the services of the stalker and his ghillie or ponyman, who is responsible for retrieving carcases (see Plate 1.7), but usually retains ownership of the

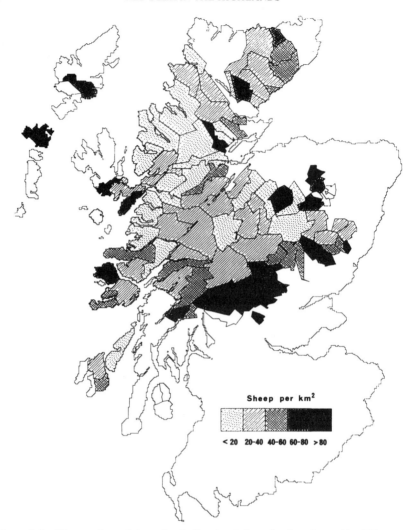

Figure 1.2 The number of sheep (excluding lambs) per km² registered in different parishes covered by the Red Deer Commission's counts. Figures were obtained from the Department of Agriculture and Fisheries for Scotland and are for June census, 1981.

venison. Hinds are culled in winter, usually by the stalker or by other estate staff (see Plate 1.8). The total reported cull of red deer is around forty thousand animals, producing an income of around £2 million in 1979 from the sale of venison and other deer parts and about £500,000 from stalking lets[4,30,31]. However, this simple calculation of direct revenue is a gross underestimate of the importance of deer to the region. Few Highland estates are self-supporting and most are subsidized (often heavily) by the external interests and activities of their owners. Their maintenance is closely bound up with the continuing attraction of deer stalking, grouse shooting and salmon fishing.

Plate 1.6 (a)

Plate 1.6 (b)

Plate 1.6 (c)

Plate 1.6 Stalking stags in the traditional manner in the Western Highlands. (a) Stalker leads client in the initial approach (b) crawling into position (c) inching into position for the shot (d) taking the shot. (Photographs: Lea MacNally.)

1.3   THE HISTORY AND PRE-HISTORY OF RED DEER

Though they extend into the tropics, deer (*Cervidae*) have always been principally confined to temperate lands (Figure 1.3). Deer-like animals first became distinct from giraffe-like species around 30 million years ago. The most ancient species were of small or medium size, and males carried long canines, similar to those of Chinese water deer (*Hydropotes* spp.)[33]. The first real deer appeared in Eurasia about twenty million years ago and resembled modern musk deer. By fifteen million years ago, species with deciduous antlers

Plate 1.7 The stalker and two ghillies bringing two stags off the hill on Rhum. (Photograph: Brian Mitchell.)

Plate 1.8 Spying for hinds in snow in Wester Ross. (Photograph: Lea MacNally.)

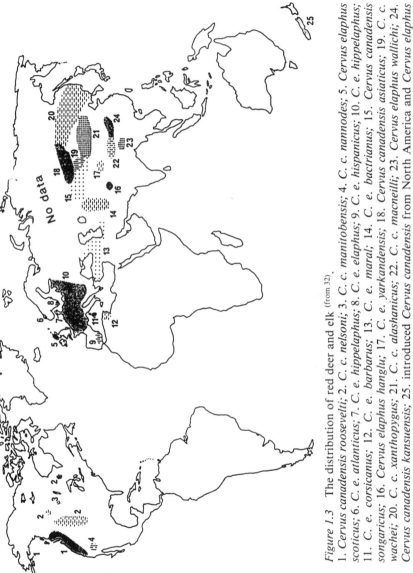

Figure 1.3   The distribution of red deer and elk [(from 32)].
1. *Cervus canadensis roosevelti*; 2. *C. c. nelsoni*; 3. *C. c. manitobensis*; 4. *C. c. nannodes*; 5. *Cervus elaphus scoticus*; 6. *C. e. atlanticus*; 7. *C. e. hippelaphus*; 8. *C. e. elaphus*; 9. *C. e. hispanicus*; 10. *C. e. hippelaphus*; 11. *C. e. corsicanus*; 12. *C. e. maral*; 13. *C. e. barbarus*; 14. *C. e. bactrianus*; 15. *Cervus canadensis songaricus*; 16. *Cervus elaphus hanglu*; 17. *C. e. yarkandensis*; 18. *Cervus canadensis asiaticus*; 19. *C. c. wachei*; 20. *C. c. xanthopygus*; 21. *C. c. alashanicus*; 22. *C. c. macneilli*; 23. *Cervus elaphus wallichi*; 24. *Cervus canadensis kansuensis*; 25. introduced *Cervus canadensis* from North America and *Cervus elaphus* from Great Britain.

occurred widely in Eurasia and it was probably during this period that deer first extended their range out of marshy thickets into drier forest zones.

Deer then began to invade more open habitats and to feed extensively on grassy plants, and by eight to ten million years ago, identifiable ancestors of the genera *Cervus* and *Axis* had developed, characterized by marked differences in size and antler development between the sexes. Subsequently, members of the genus *Cervus* show a progressive complexity of antler forms as a result of ramification of the upper tines, and around three million years ago a *Cervus* species closely resembling modern red deer, carrying antlers with a simple top fork, occurred in Eurasia[33-35]. It is now usual to regard red deer (*Cervus elaphus* Linnaeus, 1758), which extend from western Europe to central Asia, as conspecific with the North American wapiti (*Cervus canadensis* Erxleben, 1777)[36,37] (Figure 1.3).

Prehistoric red deer in Europe were very much larger than contemporary populations[35-40]. Body size reached its peak during the last glaciation and has gradually declined until the present day, though contemporary red deer in mainland Europe are substantially larger than those in Scotland and have relatively large antlers. The decline in body size and relative antler size in Scottish deer is principally a result of stunting in the harsh and mineral-poor environment of the Scottish uplands for animals raised on deer farms attain weights and antler sizes comparable to those of eastern European deer[27].

1.4   RED DEER IN SCOTLAND

Red deer have existed in Scotland for at least the last 20,000 years. During most of this time they have lived in an environment that was heavily forested but probably always included substantial tracts of open country. After the retreat of the ice sheet at the end of the last glaciation around 11,000 years ago, forests of birch, willow, alder and pine spread throughout much of the Highlands. Below 500 m the bare hills of today would have been well-wooded, with birch, hazel and oak woodland in the valleys giving way to Scots pine and birch on the hill slopes. Roe deer, reindeer and moose were present, as well as lynx, bears and wolves, but the red deer were the commonest quarry of the Mesolithic hunters that spread through the country at this time.

Around 4000 years ago, farming cultures spread through the country bringing with them an economy based on the cultivation of cereals and management of sheep and cattle[41]. Local clearance of the forest by burning or cutting increased and the process of clearance accelerated in the succeeding Bronze Age (1900-250 BC) and Iron Age (150 BC – 80 AD). Equipped with iron axes, the men of the Iron Age were able to fell trees more quickly and wood was in widespread demand for smelting.

Before the end of the Middle Ages, most of the lowlands had been cleared. Wood was in strong demand for iron smelting and the smelters gradually moved north into the Highlands, bringing the iron ore with them to smelt wherever wood was available. Oak and Scots pine were also in demand for shipbuilding. By the end of the seventeenth century, much of the ancient pine forest had been cleared though large tracts still existed in some parts of the Highlands[42]. The animal populations were quickly affected. Bears are thought to have become extinct by the tenth century and reindeer by the twelfth or thirteenth. Wolves survived and were still a nuisance in the seventeenth century but, with a bounty on their head and every man's hand against them, their numbers fell. By 1750, they, too, were extinct. However, the red deer adapted to their new environment, drawing back to the remote areas of the Highlands and using high ground[41]. Their size declined but numbers were still substantial and deer drives (tainchels) were not uncommon. Throughout much of the country numbers were probably declining during the seventeenth and eighteenth centuries[41] and successive attempts were made by major land owners, like the Duke of Atholl, to legislate against poaching and indiscriminate killing[42-44]. In the second half of the eighteenth century, two important changes occurred. First, the human population of the Highlands increased rapidly, doubling in some areas between 1750 and 1800. And, second, it was discovered that Blackface and Cheviot sheep throve on the upland pastures of the Highlands. Many Highland land-owners, especially in Sutherland and the West Highlands, found it was more profitable to clear the local crofters off their ground and to let their estates as sheep walks than to maintain the ancient system of arable farming on low ground. The graziers quickly recognized the deer as a competitor to their flocks and after 1750 deer numbers over much of the country fell further. Though pockets of deer probably existed in many parts of the Highlands, by 1811 only six deer forests had substantial numbers of deer on their ground

Table 1.1 Numbers of deer culled legally per year before 1939[46]

| | Pre-1939 War Average number killed | | |
	(i) Stags	(ii) Hinds	(iii) Total
Aberdeenshire	498	489	987
Angus	264	215	479
Argyllshire			
Mainland	924	795	1719
Isles	440	451	891
Total	1346	1246	2610
Banffshire	117	137	254
Buteshire	47	51	98
Caithness	190	176	366
Dunbartonshire	18	14	32
Inverness-shire			
Mainland	2816	2322	5138
Isles	224	155	379
Total	3040	2477	5517
Kincardineshire	37	105	142
Miscellaneous			
Counties	24	39	63
Perthshire	1176	1544	2720
Ross and Cromarty			
Mainland	2003	1257	3260
Isles	142	107	249
Total	2145	1364	3509
Stirlingshire	24	17	41
Sutherland	834	413	1247
Total	9778	8287	18065

(Atholl, Black Mount, Glenartney, Glen Fiddich, Invercauld and Mar).

An unexpected development arrested this decline. Increased wealth, generated by the Industrial Revolution, coupled with developments in sporting guns and rifles, led to a demand for shooting in the Highlands by English gentry. At first, sporting rents were low, though they created an additional source of revenue which persuaded some Highland lairds and their tenants to conserve the remnants of their deer populations[41]. However, in the 1820s and 1830s, it became progressively more fashionable to shoot in the Highlands and a number of the larger landowners cleared their ground of sheep. By 1838, sporting rents had risen substantially, the number of deer forests had increased to forty-five[45] and attempts were made to control predators and poachers. To ensure their southern clients a satisfactory day's sport, the lairds employed full-time stalkers whose job was to get the shooting client into position and it was during this period that much of the tradition of modern deer stalking was established. Prince Albert's love of stalking combined with the purchase of Balmoral by Queen Victoria in 1852 set the seal of royal approval on the sport and deer stalking entered its heyday. Gentry and wealthy English industrialists purchased estates, built roads, bridges and substantial shooting lodges and invested in all the paraphernalia of stalking. A fall in the price of wool in the 1870s reduced the potential yield of sheep farming and the area of ground covered by deer forests increased rapidly, from just under 1 million hectares in 1883 to nearly 2 million by 1912.

Until the 1900s, few attempts were made to estimate the number of red deer in the Highlands. Isolated landowners, like Henry Evans of Jura[5], attempted to count their stock but most had no firm idea of the number of deer on their ground. In the 1890s, George Malcolm, the factor of Invergarry estate, estimated the total annual cull of deer was at least 4,650 stags and 4,555 hinds. A survey of the number of stags shot in deer forests immediately before the second world war[46] indicates a total cull of around 10,000 stags and 8,000 hinds (see Table 1.1).

Deer numbers probably declined between 1939 and 1945 as a result of increased shooting combined with poaching though estimates of the extent of the decline vary widely, ranging from around 20% to over 50%. In the immediate post-war years, concern over the decline in deer numbers and public reaction to organised poaching and regular marauding by deer onto farmland led to increasing interest in assessing the number of deer in the Highlands. In 1952, Frank Fraser Darling was appointed by the Nature Conservancy to survey Scottish deer populations and systematic counting began in 1953. Over the next seven years, the Nature Conservancy's stalkers covered around a third of all deer ground in Scotland and estimated the total population to be about 155,000.

Over the same period, attempts were made to introduce legislation enforcing close seasons and increasing penalties for poaching, finally leading to the Deer (Scotland) Act of 1959. Among the provisions of the Act were the establishment of legal close seasons for stags (21 October – 30 June) and hinds (16 February – 20 October) and the establishment of an official body, the Red Deer Commission, with statutory duties of furthering the conservation and control of red deer in Scotland. The right of occupiers of agricultural holdings to kill deer trespassing on enclosed land at any time of year had been established by the Agriculture (Scotland) Act of 1948.

Thirty years later, the Commission is still active. Its members are selected by the Secretary of State for Scotland and, in addition to the Chairman, include members nominated by conservation bodies and sporting, forestry, farming and landowning interests. Since 1959, the Commission's field team has counted an average of 400,000 hectares each year, though this varies widely between years, publishing the results in its Annual Reports[4]. Between 1961 and 1970, the Commission's stalkers covered around 80% of deer ground in the Highlands, providing the first reliable estimate of the total Scottish population living on the open hill. Within this area, they counted 152,000 deer and estimated the total population at 185,000. In addition, the Commission's staff monitor the annual cull, collating annual returns of the numbers of animals shot provided by estates. In the next chapter we describe changes in deer numbers since 1959 and estimates of spatial variation in population density throughout the Highlands, based on the Red Deer Commission's counts.

1.5 SUMMARY

1.1   Since the factors affecting red deer numbers and performance vary, universal prescriptions for deer management are unlikely to be successful and an understanding of the likely consequences of environmental changes, combined with local experience provides the most promising basis for management. In this book, we attempt to synthesize studies of the ecology of red deer in the Highlands, drawing on the Red Deer Commission's extensive counts, detailed studies of particular populations and research on the physiology of growth, reproduction and digestion in red deer. Two themes recur throughout all eight chapters − the marginal nature of Highland habitats for red deer and the extent to which behaviour, ecology and population dynamics differ between hinds and stags.

1.2−1.4 Red deer populations have probably been present in the Highlands since the end of the last Ice Age. Prehistoric red deer were substantially larger than contemporary animals but, following the clearance of the ancient forests, Scottish red deer retreated to the Highlands and their body size declined. Numbers reached their lowest ebb by the end of the eighteenth century but demand for sport in the nineteenth century led to increased protection and numbers rose until the Second World War. Shortly after this, the first reliable estimates suggested that at least 155,000 were present in the Highlands and by 1970 this had risen to 185,000.

REFERENCES

1. Darling, F. F. (1937). *A Herd of Red Deer*. O.U.P., London.
2. Mitchell, B., Staines, B. W. & Welch, D. (1977). *Ecology of Red Deer: a Research Review Relevant to their Management*. Inst. of Terrestrial Ecology, Cambridge.
3. Clutton-Brock, T. H., Guinness, F. E. & Albon, S. D. (1982). *Red Deer: Behavior and Ecology of Two Sexes*. University of Chicago Press, Chicago.
4. *Red Deer Commission Annual Reports* (1961−1983). H.M.S.O., Edinburgh.
5. Evans, H. (1890). *Some Account of Jura Red Deer*. Private publication, Carter, Derby.

6. Mitchell, B. & Crisp, J. M. (1981). 'Some properties of red deer (*Cervus elaphus*) at exceptionally high population density in Scotland'. *J. Zool.*, **193**, 157–169.

7. Ratcliffe, P. R. (1984a). 'Population dynamics of red deer (*Cervus elaphus* L.) in Scottish commercial forests'. *Proc. Roy. Soc. Edinb.*, **82B**, 291–302.

8. Ratcliffe, P. R. (1984b). 'Population density and reproduction of red deer in Scottish commercial forests'. *Acta Zool. Fenn.*, **172**, 191–192.

9. Ratcliffe, P. R. (1987). 'Red deer population changes in woodland and the independent assessment of population size'. In: *Mammal Population Studies*, ed. S. Harris. Symp. Zoological Society, Lond., **58**, 153–165.

10. Osborne, B. C. (1984). 'Habitat use by red deer (*Cervus elaphus*) and hill sheep in the west Highlands'. *J. App. Ecol.* **21**, 497–506.

11. Lowe, V. P. W. (1969). 'Population dynamics of the red deer (*Cervus elaphus*) on Rhum'. *J. Anim. Ecol.* **38**, 425–457.

12. Lowe, V. P. W. (1971). 'Some effects of a change in estate management on a deer population'. In: *The Scientific Management of Animal and Plant Communities for Conservation*, ed. Duffey, E. & Watt, A. S., pp. 437–445. Blackwell Scientific Publications, Oxford.

13. Mitchell, B., McCowan, D. & Nicholson, I. A. (1976). 'Annual cycles of body weight and condition in Scottish red deer, *Cervus elaphus*'. *J. Zool. Lond.*, **180**, 107–127.

14. Mutch, W. E. S., Lockie, J. D. & Cooper, A. N. (1976). *The Red Deer in South Ross: a Report on Wildlife Management in the Scottish Highlands*. Department of Forestry & Natural Resources, University of Edinburgh.

15. Grace, J. & Easterbee, N. (1979). 'The natural shelter for red deer (*Cervus elaphus*) in a Scottish glen'. *J. Appl. Ecol.*, **16**, 37–48.

16. Hewson, R. (1976). 'Grazing by mountain hare (*Lepus timidus*), red deer (*Cervus elaphus*) and red grouse (*Lagopus l. scotticus*) on heather moorland in N.E. Scotland'. *J. Appl. Ecol.*, **13**, 657–666.

17. Moss, R., Welch, D. & Rothery, P. (1981). 'Effects of grazing by mountain hares and red deer on the production and chemical composition of heather'. *J. Appl. Ecol.*, **18**, 487–496.

18. Mitchell, B. (1973). 'The reproductive performance of wild Scottish red deer *Cervus elaphus*'. *J. Reprod. Fert. Suppl.*, **19**, 271–285.

19. Watson, A. (1971). 'Climate and the antler-shedding and performance of red deer in North-east Scotland'. *J. Appl. Ecol.*, **8**, 53–68.

20. Staines, B. W. (1970). *The Management and Dispersion of a Red Deer Population in Glen Dye, Kincardineshire*. Unpubl. Ph.D. thesis. University of Aberdeen.

21. Staines, B. (1978). 'The dynamics and performance of a declining

population of red deer (*Cervus elaphus*)'. *J. Zool. Lond.*, **184**, 403–419.

22. Mitchell, B. (1984). 'Some effects of the severe winter of 1962/63 on red deer hinds and calves in N.E. Scotland'. *Deer*, **6**, 81–84.

23. Mitchell, B., McCowan, D. & Parish, T. (1986). 'Performance and population dynamics in relation to management of red deer *Cervus elaphus* at Glenfeshie, Inverness-shire, Scotland'. *Biological Conservation*, **37**, 237–267.

24. Staines, B. W., Crisp, J. M. & Parish, T. (1982). 'Differences in food quality in red deer (*Cervus elaphus*) stags and hinds in winter'. *J. Appl. Ecol.*, **19**, 65–77.

25. Colquhoun, I. R. (1971). *The Grazing Ecology of Red Deer and Blackface Sheep in Perthshire, Scotland*. Unpublished Ph.D. thesis, Edinburgh.

26. Mitchell, B. unpublished data.

27. Blaxter, K. L., Kay, R. N. B., Sharman, G. A. M., Cunningham, J. M. M. & Hamilton, W. J. (1974). *Farming the Red Deer*. H.M.S.O., London.

28. Blaxter, K. L., Kay, R. N. B., Sharman, G. A. M., Cunningham, J. M. M., Easie, J. & Hamilton, W. J. (1988). *Farming the Red Deer*, H.M.S.O., London.

29. Kay, R. N. B. & Staines, B. W. (1981). 'The nutrition of red deer (*Cervus elaphus*)'. *Nutr. Abstr. Rev.*, **51**, 601–622.

30. Bryden, J. M. (1979). 'Deer and the Highland Economy'. In: *The Next Twenty Years*. pp.17–21. Red Deer Commission, Inverness.

31. Jarvis, E. (1980). *The Red Deer Industry, Finance and Employment 1978/79*. The Scottish Landowners' Federation, Edinburgh.

32. Whitehead, G. K. (1972). *Deer of the World*. Constable, London.

33. Flerov, K. K. (1952). *Fauna of the U.S.S.R. Mammals - Musk Deer and Deer*. Vol. I. U.S.S.R. Academy of Sciences, Moscow. Translated by the Israel Program of Scientific Translation.

34. Beninde, J. (1937). *Zur Naturgeschichte des Rothirsches. Monographie Wild-säugetiere*. Bd. IV. Leipzig.

35. Lister, A. M. (1984). 'Evolutionary and ecological origins of British deer'. *Proc. Roy. Soc. Edinb.*, **82B**, 205–229.

36. Ellerman, J. R. & Morrison-Scott, T. C. S. (1951). *Check List of Palearctic and Indian mammals, 1758–1946*. British Museum, London.

37. Corbet, G. B. (1978). *The Mammals of the Palearctic Region: a Taxonomic Review*. British Museum of Natural History, London.

38. Delpech, F. & Suire, C. (1974). *La Faune Mésolithique et post-Mesolithique du Gisement de Rouffignac*. Publ. Institut. d'Art Préhistorique de l'Université de Toulouse-le-Mirail. Meon-Institut Art Préhistorique II Fouffignac Fasc. 2.

39. Huxley, J. S. (1931). 'The relative size of antlers in deer'. *Proc. Zool. Soc. Lond.* 819–864.
40. Huxley, J. S. (1932). *Problems of Relative Growth.* MacVeagh, London.
41. Hart-Davies, D. (1978). *Monarchs of the Glen: a History of Deerstalking in the Scottish Highlands.* Cape, London.
42. Nethersole-Thompson, D. & Watson, A. (1983). *The Cairngorms.* Collins, London.
43. Watson, A. (1983). 'Eighteenth century deer numbers and pine regeneration near Braemar, Scotland'. *Biological Conservation*, **25**, 289–325.
44. Watson, A. & Allan, E. (1986). Papers Relating to Game Poaching on Deeside, 1766–1832. Northern Scotland **7**, 39–45.
45. Scrope, W. (1897). *Days of Deer Stalking in the Scottish Highlands.* John Murray, London.
46. Whitehead, G. K. (1964). *The Deer Forests of Great Britain and Ireland.* Routledge and Kegan Paul, London.

2 Red Deer Populations

2.1   INTRODUCTION

Numbers of red deer in the Highlands have changed substantially over the last thirty years and their population density varies widely between parts of the country. In this chapter, we describe changes in population density and investigate their likely causes. Section 2.2 describes the system of deer counts on which our estimates of population density are based while Section 2.3 describes spatial variation in deer density and its likely causes. Section 2.4 describes culling regimes throughout the Highlands while Section 2.5 reviews some of the implications of these results for deer management.

2.2   DEER COUNTS AND CHANGES IN POPULATION
2.2   DENSITY

For counting purposes, the Red Deer Commission divides Scotland into 41 counting blocks (see Figure 2.1), each sufficiently large to encompass the ranges of both sexes with a perimeter of natural or man-made barriers which are thought to prevent any substantial movement in or out[1,2]. When each block is covered, the team attempts to count all animals with as little error as possible. Areas of woodland and forestry plantations are excluded since it is impossible to count deer reliably within them using conventional counting techniques.

The Commission's original objective was to cover as much of the 3.14 million hectares of open deer ground as possible[2]. Recounts of areas were made on an opportunistic basis or in response to requests from landowners or complaints from farmers, though the Commission is currently engaged in completing a second entire count. Of the total area of ground in the range of red deer in the Highlands, 35.6% has now been covered three or more times, 29% twice, 21.5% once and 13% has yet to be covered. In addition, the deer population of the Isle of Rhum (10,000 hectares) has been counted by the Commission each year since 1966 with the exception of 1969 and 1973, while Glenfeshie was counted each year between 1967 and 1974.

Counts are mostly carried out in late winter or early spring when conditions are sufficiently severe to keep the deer on low ground[1]. The counting team typically consists of 8–10 experienced stalkers equipped with binoculars, telescopes and two-way radios. Each stalker has a 1:50,000 Ordnance Survey map and records all animals

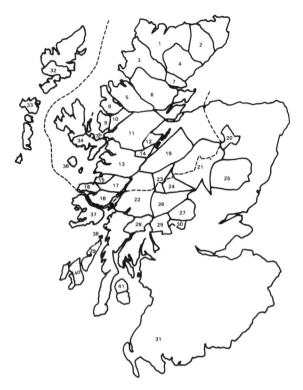

Figure 2.1 The Red Deer Commission's counting blocks. The dashed line shows the boundary of the (administrative) Highland Region and some of the analyses described below were restricted to this area:
1. N. Sutherland; 2. Caithness/Sutherland; 3. W.Sutherland; 4. E.Sutherland; 5. Wester Ross; 6. North Ross; 7. Rovie/Skibo; 8. Gairloch Cons. Unit; 9. Applecross; 10. Shieldaig/Ledgowan; 11. South Ross; 12. Glenmoriston/Glenurquhart; 13. W.Inverness; 14. Ardochy/Port Clair; 15. W.Loch Shiel; 16. Ardnamurchan; 17. Conaglen/Ardgour; 18. Morvern; 19. Monadhliaths; 20. Cabrach/Glen Fiddich; 21. Cairngorm/W.Grampians; 22. Ben Nevis/Blackmount; 23. Corrour/Ben Alder/Ardverikie; 24. E.Loch Ericht; 25. E.Grampians; 26. Rannoch/S.Tay; 27. S.Loch Tay; 28. Argyll; 29. Trossachs; 30. Glenartney; 31. Galloway; 32. Harris/Lewis; 33. N. Uist; 34. Skye; 35. Scalpay; 36. Rhum; 37. Mull; 38. Scarba; 39. Jura; 40. Islay; 41. Arran.

seen, maintaining radio contact with the team members on either side of him to prevent double counts. The stalkers usually work down or across the wind to avoid driving the deer ahead of them and the line on which each day's count ends is kept as short as possible to reduce the possibility of counted deer moving ahead on to uncounted ground. Animals are classified as stags, hinds or calves and numbers seen on each day are totalled and plotted on a 1:50,000 tracing of the count area.

There are two main difficulties in using the Commission's counts to estimate changes in Highland red deer populations. The first is the assessment of their accuracy. In Appendix 1 we describe the attempts that have been made to check the consistency and accuracy of counts. These suggest that estimates of total deer numbers are reliable though individual counts of local populations may be unrepresentative due to temporary or seasonal movements of deer. However, some attempts to check the accuracy with which animals are classified suggest that stag numbers may be consistently underestimated and hind numbers consistently overestimated (see Appendix 1).

The second difficulty stems from the fact that (with the exception of Rhum) different deer blocks have been counted at irregular intervals. Since, in some years, the Commission has covered ground carrying high deer densities while, in others, it has covered areas of low density, counts in successive years do not provide representative samples which can be used to estimate changes in total numbers. This problem is compounded by the fact that population density has changed since 1961[2] with the result that numbers in blocks covered several years apart may not be comparable. To overcome this difficulty, we have standardized counts of different blocks within a common time frame using a multiple regression model that includes both year and block identity as independent variables, which we refer to as the block/year model (see Appendices 2–4). Our estimates of changes in average density are based on blocks counted two or more times (around 65% of the total deer ground).

Standardized figures derived from the multiple regression model suggest that average deer density throughout the Highlands declined from 9–10 to 6–7 animals per square kilometre between 1961 and 1969 (Figure 2.2). Subsequently, numbers began to rise, increasing to 11–13 per square kilometre by the mid-seventies. After 1976, stag density appears to have fallen while hind density has remained approximately constant until 1986 when numbers apparently rose again[4].

If these figures are converted into estimates of total population size, they suggest that total numbers on the open hill were around 216,000 ±45,000 in the early sixties, falling to 155,000 ±43,000 between 1966 and 1969 and then rising to 248,000 ±55,000 by the mid-seventies. Estimates for 1986 suggest that in early spring the total population was 297,000 ±40,000. If deer in forestry are included, the most recent estimates should probably be raised by a

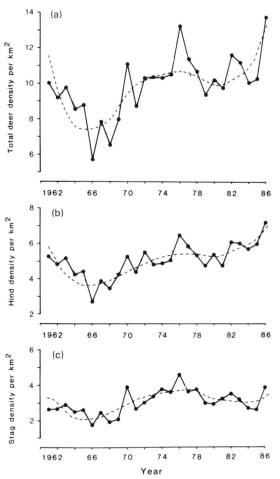

Figure 2.2 Changes in the average density of (a) all deer, including calves (b) hinds only and (c) stags only in the Highlands, 1961-1986 estimated using the block/year model (see Appendices 2-4). Estimates exclude deer in forestry plantations and are based on blocks or parts of blocks counted at least twice. The dashed line shows a polynomial curve fitted through the points, showing the likely pattern of change.

further 25–50,000[2,3]. Our figures are higher than those produced earlier by the Nature Conservancy Council and Red Deer Commission, who estimate that total numbers (excluding deer in forestry) were around 185,000 between 1960 and 1970, rising to 270,000 in 1975 and 265,000 in the early spring of 1986[4-8] though all these figures fall within the confidence limits of our estimates. These differences arise because the multiple regression model corrects estimates for ground covered in different years by the average rate of population increase (see Appendices 2–4).

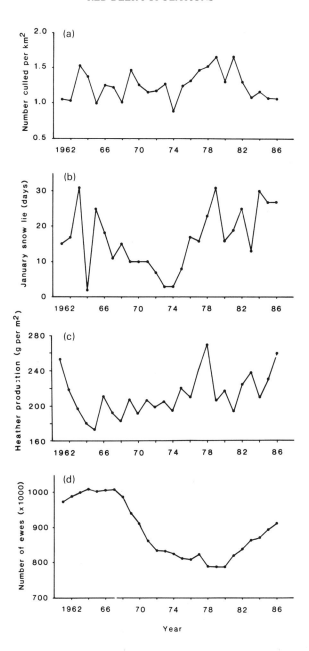

Figure 2.3 Changes in (a) the (standardized) number of animals culled per km²
(b) the number of days of snow lie in January (c) estimated heather production per
year and (d) the number of ewes registered in the Highland and N.E. Grampian
Regions in the June census prior to the count between 1961 and 1986.

At least three environmental changes may have contributed to changes in deer numbers since 1961. Between 1967 and 1975, when deer populations were rising, the average duration of winter snow cover was unusually short (Figure 2.3b). As we describe in Chapter 6, detailed studies of specific deer populations indicate that prolonged snow cover increases calf and adult mortality and can have substantial effects on annual recruitment. Over the same period, summer rainfall declined and summer temperatures increased[4]. Warm, dry summers are associated with increased production of heather, the principal winter food of deer in many areas (see Chapter 6), and this could have contributed to the rise in deer numbers between 1967 and 1975 (see Figure 2.3c). Third, sheep stocks in the Highlands were relatively high in the early sixties but declined steadily between 1966 and 1979, before rising again in recent years[9]. For example, the number of ewes registered in the Western Isles, Highland Region and North East Grampian (approximately two-thirds of the area covered by the Red Deer Commission's counts) declined by around 20% between 1966 and 1978, from just over one million to less than 800,000 (Figure 2.3d). The numbers of ewes grazed on higher ground are particularly likely to have been affected[9]. As we describe in Chapter 4, sheep and deer (especially hinds) prefer similar areas of habitat and a substantial reduction in sheep numbers might be expected to increase the amount of food available to the deer.

Since changes in weather and sheep populations occurred at the same time, it is not easy to separate their effects. However, when average population density was regressed simultaneously on winter snow lie, estimated heather production (estimated from summer rainfall and temperature using the equation shown in Figure 4.3) and sheep numbers, changes were significantly correlated with heather production and sheep numbers (Figure 2.4a,b) but not with winter snow lie. The residual variation was related to the number of adults culled (Figure 2.4c). In conjunction, these three variables accounted for 68% of variation in total deer density between years (see Appendix 3). The same variables were related to variation in the density of hinds calculated separately. However, when other effects were allowed for, the density of stags was correlated with the duration of snow lie but not with changes in culling rate.

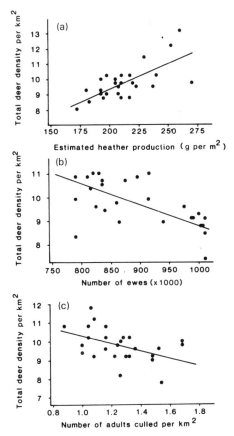

Figure 2.4 Scatter diagrams of average deer density 1961-1986 (see Figure 2.2a) plotted against (a) heather production estimated from the regression shown in Figure 4.3, (b) the number of ewes registered in the Highland and N.E. Grampian regions, (c) the estimated number of deer culled per km². In each case the fitted regression line and points are after controlling for the other two variables.

2.3   GEOGRAPHICAL VARIATION IN RED DEER DENSITY

The density of red deer and their reproductive performance vary widely throughout the Highlands. Estimated deer densities, standardized for 1986 (a year of relatively high density) are shown in Figures 2.5 – 2.7. The highest deer densities, of more than 20 deer per square kilometre, are found in the Central Highlands in Corrour, Ben Alder, Ardverikie and Glenartney and on the islands of Rhum and Jura. All these areas have high densities of both sexes, with stag densities ranging between 6 and 8 stags per square kilometre and hind densities ranging from 10 to 17 hinds per square kilometre.

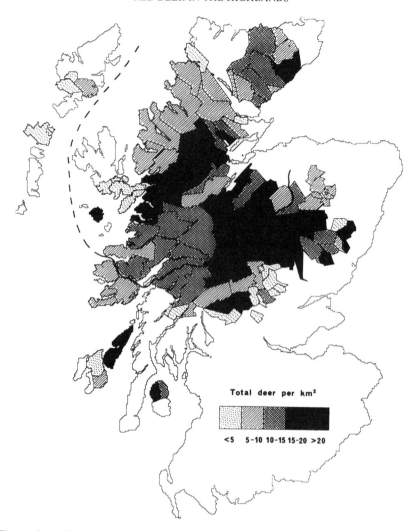

Figure 2.5 Total deer density map for parishes covered by the Red Deer Commission's counts, standardized for 1986 using the block/year model (see Appendices 2-4). The boundary of the Highland region is shown as a broken line. Some unmarked areas (e.g. N.W. Sutherland) contain red deer stocks but have yet to be counted.

Densities of between 15 and 20 deer per square kilometre are found in many areas of the Highlands, including East Caithness, South Ross, West Inverness-shire, the Monadhliaths, West Grampians, East Grampians, East Loch Ericht and the Island of Arran. In most of these areas, stag densities range between 3.5 and 6 stags per square kilometre while hind densities range from 7.5 to 10.0 hinds per square kilometre.

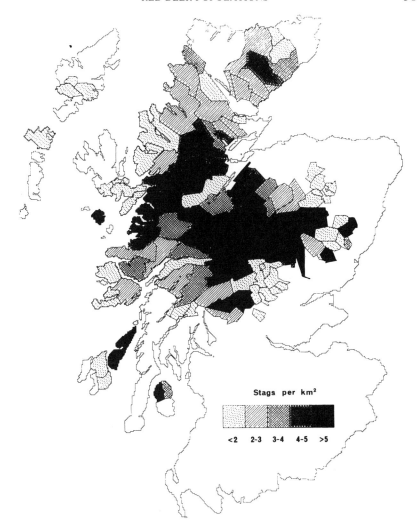

Stags per km²

<2   2-3   3-4   4-5   >5

Figure 2.6   Stag density map for parishes covered by the Red Deer Commission's counts, standardized for 1986, using the block/year model (see Appendices 2-4).

Intermediate densities of between 10 and 15 per square kilometre are found in West Sutherland, West and North Ross, West Loch Sheil, Conaglen/Ardgour, Morvern, Blackmount/Ben Nevis, Rannoch, Northern Mull and Islay. In these areas stag densities typically range between 2.5 and 3.5 per square kilometre, while hind densities vary between 5.5 and 7.5 per square kilometre.

Lower deer densities of between 5.0 and 10.0 deer per square kilometre are found in parts of West Sutherland, Wester Ross,

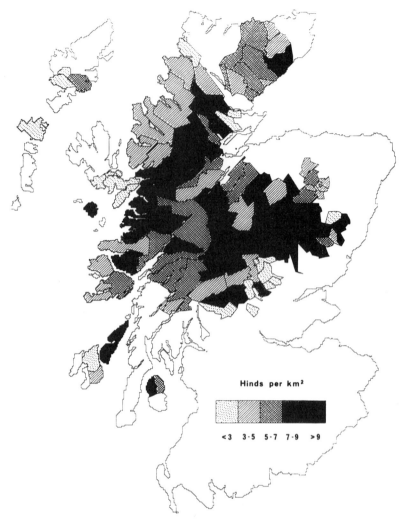

Figure 2.7   Hind density map for parishes covered by the Red Deer Commission's counts, standardized for 1986 using the block/year model (see Appendices 2–4).

Gairloch, Applecross, Shieldaig and Ledgowan, Glenmoriston, Glenurquhart, Ardochy, Glen Fiddich, South Loch Tay, Argyll, the Trossachs, Harris and Eastern and Southern Mull. In most of these areas, stag densities range between 1.0 and 3.0 stags per square kilometre while hind densities range between 2.5 and 5.5 hinds per square kilometre.

The lowest densities on accepted deer range are found in North Sutherland, North Uist, southern Skye and in some parts of the

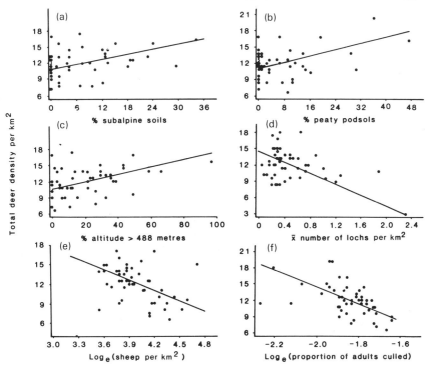

Figure 2.8 Total deer density in different parishes in the Highland Region plotted against (a) the percentage area of sub-alpine soils; (b) the percentage area of peaty podzol soils; (c) the percentage of ground over 488 m.; (d) the mean number of lochs per km^2;(e) the log$_e$ of sheep density; (f) log$_e$ of the percentage adults culled. In each plot the effects of the five other variables are allowed for (see Appendices 2 – 4). Distribution of soil types calculated from references 10-12.

eastern edge of the deer range where it abuts agricultural land. In most of these areas, stag densities are around 1.0 per square kilometre and hind densities in the region of 1.0 to 2.0 hinds per square kilometre.

Both differences in environment and culling rate probably contribute to geographical variation in population density throughout the Highlands. Six factors are independently and significantly related to differences in deer density between parishes within the Highland Region (see Figure 2.8). High deer densities are found in parishes which include relatively large areas of subalpine soils or peaty podzols and where much of the ground lies above 488 metres (Figure 2.8a,b,c). Large numbers of lochs (indicating poorly drained habitat), high culling rates and high sheep densities are associated with low deer densities (Figure 2.8d,e,f). In conjunction, these six variables account for 63% of the variation in population density between parishes (see Appendix 4). Separate analyses of variation in stag and hind density within the Highland Region (see Figures 2.6 and 2.7) suggest that the correlates of population density may differ between the sexes (Appendix 4). When other factors have been taken into account, stag density (but not hind density) declines in areas where snow cover is usually prolonged: for every 25 day increase in average snow cover per year, stag density declines by approximately 1 stag per square kilometre. In contrast, hind density (but not stag density) declines with increasing sheep numbers.

None of these correlations necessarily indicates that any of these environmental variables has a causal effect on deer density, though similar associations are found within many populations (see Chapters 5 and 6). However, they suggest that a substantial proportion of the temporal and geographical variation in deer density is probably caused by variation in environmental quality.

2.4   CULLS AND CULLING RATES

The total number of animals reported culled in the Highlands varies little from year to year (see Table 2.1). Between 1975 and 1983 an average of 14,183 stags and 16,832 hinds were shot in season plus 1,748 stags and 318 hinds out of season. In addition, between 2,500 and 3,250 calves were reported as shot each year. Some check on these figures is provided by the records kept by the venison dealers (see Table 2.1). These figures are not precisely comparable with estate returns since estates usually retain around 8% of carcases for their own use and some are left on the hill, while game dealers commonly classify the carcases of calves as hinds. Despite these difficulties, comparison of estate returns with venison dealers' figures show that the numbers of stags shot in season closely parallels the number of carcases handled by dealers, while around 9% more hinds are handled than are reported shot. However, if it is assumed that all the 2,500 calves shot each year appear in the dealers' books as hinds, the discrepancy between the reported cull and the dealers' records is small. Reported culls out of season (mostly animals raiding farmland or forestry) are considerably lower than the number of carcases handled, though it is not clear what proportion of these animals belong to populations resident on the open hill. In addition, an unknown number of animals will be killed illegally.

Table 2.1 Numbers of animals killed by estates and purchased by venison dealers, 1975–1983 to 15th February of each year[7,8].

| Year | Summary of estate returns | | | | | | Information from venison dealers' records* | | | | |
| | Stags | | Hinds excluding calves | | Calves | Total† | Stags | | Hinds and calves | | Total |
	In season	Out of season	In season	Out of season			In season	Out of season	In season	Out of season	
1975/76	12,260	1,321	18,113	83	No data	31,777	11,099	2,001	16,863	330	30,293
1976/77	14,856	1,938	19,681	192	No data	36,667	14,163	3,827	21,298	861	40,149
1978/79	14,382	2,097	17,328	320	No data	34,127	14,608	2,985	19,338	1,194	38,125
1979/80	13,846	1,664	16,282	373	No data	31,165	13,938	3,467	16,794	886	35,085
1980/81	14,644	1,303	15,072	299	2,370	31,318	16,725	2,676	17,479	908	37,788
1981/82	15,100	1,599	15,658	473	2,615	32,830	16,177	2,920	18,359	675	38,131
1982/83	14,526	1,928	17,433	415	3,264	34,302	14,659	2,790	20,587	1,433	39,469
1983/84	13,374	1,626	14,676	417	2,516	30,093	12,536	2,254	14,665	1,874	31,329
Mean	14,183	1,748	16,832	318	2,691	33,090	14,275	3,000	18,330	1,069	36,674

*These figures include kills on lands other than estates.

†Includes red deer retained by estates for own use.

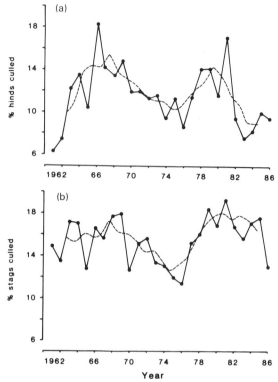

Figure 2.9 Percentages of hinds and stags culled in season 1961-1986 based on blocks counted at least twice by the Red Deer Commission. For methods of calculation, see Appendices 2-4. Interrupted lines show three-year running averages fitted through the points illustrating the likely pattern of changes.

To estimate changes in the rate of culling since 1961, we divided the reported number of animals killed in season in each block by the estimated number of deer in the block in spring (our estimates are again based on the sample of blocks counted at least twice, see Appendices 2-4). Culling rates, calculated by this method, are shown in Figure 2.9. Year to year fluctuations may be partly caused by the problems of calculating culling rate and we prefer to rely on the three year running averages fitted through the points. Our estimates suggest that culling rates were relatively high in the sixties when deer numbers were comparatively low, then fell between 1968 and 1975 as deer density rose. Subsequently, the percentage of hinds culled rose between 1975 and 1979 and then declined while the percentage of stags culled increased to around 18% and remains around this level (Figure 2.9).

The percentage of animals culled annually also varies throughout the Highlands, with relatively high culling rates around the periphery of the deer range in the eastern and southern Highlands, and lower rates in the less accessible areas of the north and west coast (Figure 2.10). Figures standardized for 1986 suggest that the proportion of hinds culled per block ranged from around 2% to over 25% while stag culls ranged from 6% to over 30%. These figures *exclude* calves and animals culled out of season and the inclusion of these categories would probably raise average stag culls by between 1% and 3% of the total population and hind culls by less than 1% (see Table 2.1).

Our analysis of the culling figures suggests that throughout much of the Highlands, the number of hinds culled in season is lower (often substantially lower) than the number recruited each year (see Chapter 5). Even if we assume that actual hind culls are 1% higher than legal in-season culls (see above) and that 14% of hinds less than one year old can be culled each year without reducing population size (see Chapter 8), then in 1986 more than 75% of blocks were culling fewer hinds than the number of animals that were probably recruited each year (see Figure 2.10). In contrast, if we assume that the real rate at which stags are culled is 3% higher than our estimated rate (see above), then over 70% of blocks are culling stags at or above the rate of recruitment. This difference may help to explain why, after 1975, hind numbers were stable or even rose slightly while stag numbers declined. However, these estimates do not allow for any misclassification in counts. If it were the case that stag numbers were consistently underestimated by 15% in counts and hind numbers were overestimated by 25% (see Appendix 1), the average (total) stag cull in 1986 would fall from around 15% to 13% while average (total) hind cull would rise from around 9% to 11%.

2.5 IMPLICATIONS FOR MANAGEMENT

The results described in Sections 2.1-2.4 have two important implications for the management of Highland red deer. First, they show that large differences in the population density of red deer exist which are probably caused partly by differences in environmental quality, partly by competition with sheep and partly by variation in culling rates. By improving environmental quality, it should be possible to increase deer density and improve growth and development: we return to this topic in Chapter 4. Conversely, by increasing sheep stocks or enclosing low ground for forestry, deer numbers may be substantially reduced. There is some evidence that different factors may affect the density of hinds and stags. In particular, hind density (but not stag density) declines in areas where sheep are abundant while stag density (but not hind density) declines where temperatures are low and snow cover is prolonged (see Appendices 3 and 4). This may indicate that the addition or removal of sheep is more likely to affect hinds than stags while access to shelter or lower ground could have more influence on stags than hinds.

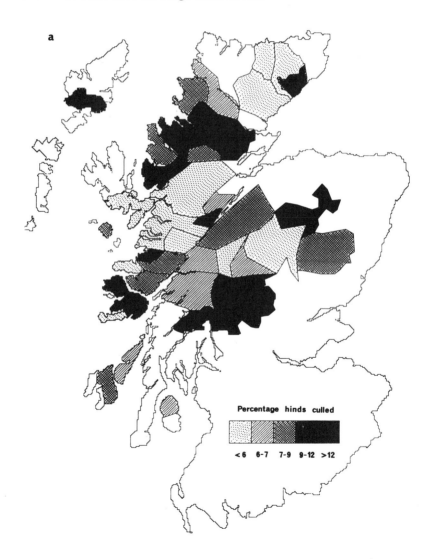

Percentage hinds culled

<6   6-7   7-9   9-12   >12

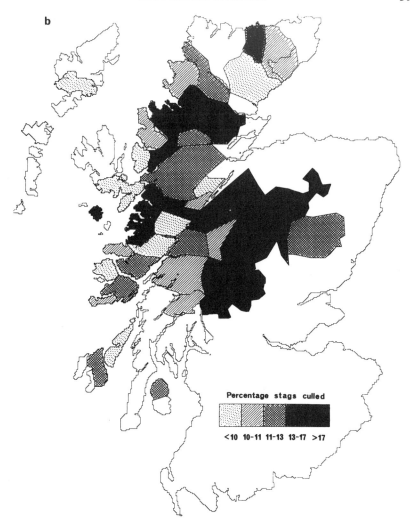

Figure 2.10 Estimates of the percentage of (a) hinds and (b) stags culled in different blocks counted by the Red Deer Commission, standardized for 1986. The percentage of animals culled is calculated as the number of animals reported killed in season divided by the number of animals estimated to be in the block plus the number of animals killed multiplied by 100 (see Appendices 2-4). Estimates exclude calves and animals culled out of season: their inclusion would probably raise average culling rates by a further 1% for hinds and 2-3% for stags (see Table 2.1).

Second, the results emphasize the need for decisions about culling to be based on regular estimates of population size and recruitment. Though they may vary little between successive years, neither population size nor recruitment rate are stable in the longer term (see

Chapters 5, 6 and 8) and unless culling rates are adjusted to these changes, they are likely either to reduce deer numbers or to fail to control them. Annual or biennial estimates of deer populations are highly desirable. These need to be integrated at the level of natural population units rather than estates, for unless smaller units of ground are covered several times in succession, counts may be unrepresentative due to temporary deer movements (see Appendix 1).

2.6 SUMMARY

2.1 – 2.2 Deer numbers in the Highlands appear to have declined in the early sixties before rising again in the late sixties and early seventies. Since 1976, stag numbers appear to have remained constant or to have declined while hind numbers have risen slightly. The rise in deer numbers in the late sixties and early seventies occurred at the same time as a substantial decline in sheep numbers. At the same time there was an amelioration in winter weather and a decline in summer rainfall which may have improved heather production. All three changes may have contributed to variation in deer density.

2.3 Density on accepted deer range varies between counting blocks from less than 5 deer per square kilometre to over 30 deer per square kilometre. Differences in hind densities are related to differences in altitude, the abundance of well-drained and mineralised soils and the number of sheep present, as well as to culling rate, while differences in stag density are related to altitude, soil type, culling rate and to winter weather.

2.4 Culling rates (the percentage of the spring population excluding calves killed in the subsequent season) range from less than 5% to over 20%. In many areas of the Highlands, hind culls appear to be lower than the number of animals recruited while stag culls approach or exceed recruitment.

2.5 These results indicate that environmental changes, including the exclosure of low ground for forestry and alteration in sheep numbers, are likely to affect red deer numbers. In addition, they show that neither population size nor recruitment is stable from year to year and emphasize the need for regular estimates of population density as a basis for management decisions.

REFERENCES

1. Red Deer Commission (1981). *Red Deer Management*. H.M.S.O., London.
2. Stewart, L. K. (1986). 'Red deer and their influence on vegetation management in Northern Britain'. *Deer*, **6**, 345 – 346.

3. Ratcliffe, P. R. (1987). 'Red deer population changes in woodland and the independent assessment of population size'. In: *Mammal Population Studies,* ed. S. Harris, Symp. Zool. Soc., Lond., **58**, 153–165.

4. Albon, S. D. & Clutton-Brock, T. H. (1988). 'Climate and the population dynamics of red deer in Scotland'. In: *Ecological Change in the Uplands*, ed. M. B. Usher and D. Thompson, pp. 93–107. Blackwells, Oxford.

5. *Red Deer Commission Annual Report*, 1970. H.M.S.O., London.

6. *Red Deer Commission Annual Report*, 1976. H.M.S.O., London.

7. Stewart, L. K. (1988) 'Deer in Scotland'. In: *The Changing Scene.* Red Deer Commission, Inverness.

8. *Red Deer Commission Annual Report*, 1986. H.M.S.O., London.

9. Gordon-Duff-Pennington, P. T. (1979). 'Farming developments in the red deer range'. In: *The Next Twenty Years*, 11–18, Red Deer Commission, Inverness.

10. Futty, D. W. & Towers, W. (1982). *Soil and Land Capability for Agriculture, Northern Scotland*, Sheet 3. Macaulay Institute for Soil Research, Aberdeen.

11. Bibby, J. S., Hudson, G. & Henderson, D. J. (1982). *Soil and Land Capability for Agriculture, Western Scotland*, Sheet 4. Macaulay Institute for Soil Research, Aberdeen.

12. Walker, A.D., Campbell, G.G.B., Heslop, R.E.F., Gould, J.H., Laing, D., Shipley, D. M. & Wright, G. C. (1982). *Soil and Land Capability for Agriculture, Eastern Scotland*, Sheet 5. Macaulay Institute for Soil Research, Aberdeen.

3 Social Behaviour, Reproduction, Growth and Survival

3.1 INTRODUCTION

To manage animal populations, it is necessary to understand the factors affecting recruitment and survival. In this chapter, we describe what is known of the social behaviour and dispersal of Highland red deer (Section 3.2), their reproduction (Section 3.3), the survival of their calves (Section 3.4) and their growth (Section 3.5) as well as the effects of age and reproductive history on breeding success (Sections 3.6 and 3.7). In the final section, we outline the principal implications of these results for management.

As we described in Chapter 1, much of the detailed knowledge of red deer demography is based on studies at two sites: the Isle of Rhum on the west coast, and at Glenfeshie in the central Highlands (see p.3). Of the work on Rhum, the most detailed has been carried out on the population of the North Block. This area has not been culled since 1972 and, as a result, reproductive performance is inferior compared to many mainland populations. Nevertheless, the same factors that affect fecundity, growth and survival in the North Block of Rhum are likely to be at work in other deer populations.

3.2 SOCIAL BEHAVIOUR AND DISPERSAL

In most parts of the Highlands, hinds are usually seen in groups of two to fifty or more. Individuals have well defined home ranges which they seldom leave. The average size of home ranges varies widely between populations, from around one square kilometre (40 acres) to more than five square kilometres[1,2]. On Rhum, a hind's daughters usually adopt home ranges overlapping that of their mother, though they sometimes extend their ranges beyond these boundaries[3]. Hinds usually associate with their relatives and small family parties of hinds commonly consist of a grandmother and her daughters and granddaughters (Plate 3.1). Neighbouring lineages or matrilines of hinds have overlapping home ranges (see Figure 3.1) and larger parties form which consist of the members of several lineages though these are unstable in membership from hour to hour as small parties of hinds join and leave the group. As the size of hind groups increases, the reproductive performance of their members falls[3]. Within hind groups, larger individuals can consistently displace smaller animals from feeding sites. These dominant hinds show superior body condition and reproductive performance[4].

(a)

(b)

Plate 3.1 (a) A group of hinds consisting of a grandmother (lower, right), her mature daughter (top left) and three granddaughters. (Photograph: T. H. Clutton-Brock.) (b) Related hinds commonly have similar markings. This group consists of a grandmother (third from the left), her two daughters (second from left and furthest right) and their two calves. With the exception of the middle calf, all members of the family have well defined dark markings at the base of the tail. (Photograph: Fiona Guinness.)

Figure 3.1   Core areas of matrilineal hind groups using the North Block study area on Rhum[3]. Each ellipse shows the smallest area accounting for 65% of all observations of group members closest to the centre of their range. Numbers refer to the identity of matrilines, not to their size.

Stags are less closely hefted to a particular area and individuals sometimes have separate summer and winter ranges as well as separate rutting areas (see below). When stags leave their mothers' groups, usually during their third or fourth year of life, they wander widely before adopting a new home range[2]. Stags tend to adopt winter ranges in areas adjacent to but separate from the main hind groups. Like hind groups, parties of stags are temporary and vary in membership from hour to hour and day to day though individuals can develop particular attachments to each other[5].

An important consequence of the close social bonds that exist between related hinds and their reluctance to leave the area where they are born is that stags disperse more widely than hinds. In our study area on Rhum, around 50% of all stags born in the North

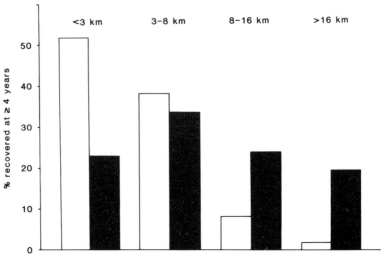

Figure 3.2 Distances between marking and recovery sites for samples of 110 hind calves and 113 stag calves marked in the West Grampians by the Red Deer Commission in 1967-1983 and recovered four or more years later[6]. Open columns, hinds and close columns stags.

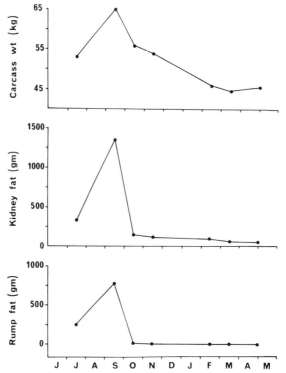

Figure 3.3 Seasonal changes in body weight and condition of five- to ten- year old stags on Rhum[8].

Plate 3.2.   A mature stag grazing on the machair on Rhum in early August. In late July or early August the velvet frays and peels, exposing sharp new antler points. (Photograph: Fiona Guinness.)

Block disperse to permanent home ranges throughout the rest of the island. The Red Deer Commission's marking programme in the West Grampians shows that only 10% of hinds are shot over 8 km (5 miles) from their birth area compared with more than 40% of stags[6] (see Figure 3.2) though in this case it is not possible to distinguish permanent emigration from temporary emigration during the rut (see below). However, in the great majority of non-migratory mammals, males disperse from their natal areas while most females adopt home ranges close to their own birth site[7].

3.3   REPRODUCTION

In the second half of the summer, stags gain weight (see Figure 3.3).

In July, their testes begin to grow rapidly, tripling in weight by early September[9]. The concentration of the male hormone, testosterone, in their blood rises, triggering antler cleaning and subsequently the development of neck muscles and mane (Plate 3.2). In late September, stag groups fragment, individuals moving to their traditional rutting grounds in areas heavily used by hinds[10]. Long-term records of individual stags on Rhum show that young stags wander widely during the rut while mature stags usually return to the area where they first held a harem successfully[2].

Once on the rutting grounds, stags herd together groups of hinds, defending their harems, day and night, from other stags (Plates 3.3, 3.4). On Rhum, fights are frequent and around one fifth of all rutting stags show some sign of injury each year[11]. The fighting success of stags depends on their body size, condition and weight and is closely related to the size of their harems and the number of hinds with which they mate[11]. The most successful stags father up to a dozen or more calves each rut whereas smaller and less success-

Plate 3.3 (a)

Plate 3.3 (a) A ten-year-old stag in his prime mounts an estrous hind. (Photograph: Fiona Guinness.) (b) Two mature stags fight for possession of a harem. Fights can last up to 20 minutes and around one in five lead to some form of injury. (Photograph: T. H. Clutton-Brock.)

ful animals commonly fail to breed altogether. Though large, mature stags are usually more successful than young or small animals, there is no indication that stags with relatively large antlers for their size are particularly successful breeders[11,12]. The fact that stags that have broken the main beam of one or more of their antlers are quickly beaten[13] does not contradict this, for stags that have recently lost their antlers are usually unable to fight effectively.

Around the end of September, the first hinds come into estrus (Figure 3.4) and the number of conceptions rises to a peak in the second or third weeks of October (Figure 3.5). Most hinds are in estrus for 6-24 hours and, during this time, usually show interest in the stag, licking him and sometimes mounting him[16]. Conception is highly synchronized with over 80% of all conceptions occurring within a month, though a small number of hinds conceive in

(a)

(b)

Plate 3.4　(a) Stags roar up to three times per minute throughout the 24 hours while they are holding harems. Their roaring rate reflects their fighting ability. (Photograph: T.H. Clutton-Brock.) (b) A mature stag chases a yearling male (knobber) from his harem. Knobbers have usually been expelled by the end of the first week in October. Some stags also evict calves from their harems. (Photograph: T. H. Clutton-Brock.)

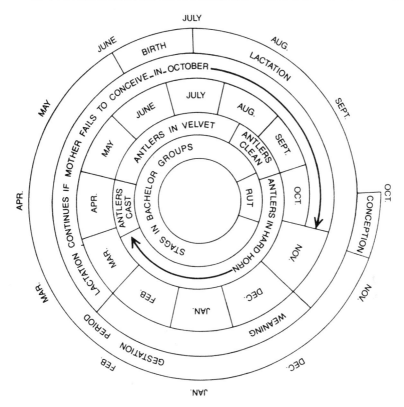

Figure 3.4 Reproductive cycle of Scottish red deer. The outer two rings depict the cycle for hinds. The inner two rings relate to the cycle for stags. The mating season occurs in October, when more than 80% of the hinds conceive. Calves are born in June and most are weaned six or seven months later if the mother conceives again but not until about 18 months after birth if the mother fails to conceive in the second autumn. The outer ring of the cycle for stags shows the monthly state of the antlers.

November and December (Figure 3.5). Hinds in the same harem tend to be synchronous in their conception dates, possibly using olfactory cues[17]. However, not all hinds produce a calf each year. We refer to mature hinds (over 4 years old) that have either failed to breed or have lost their calf within a few weeks of birth (consequently avoiding the costs of lactation) as yeld hinds.

Stags typically mount a hind several times before ejaculating, leaping clear of the ground when they ejaculate. It used to be thought that most mating occurred at night but systematic observation shows that red deer mate throughout the day and night with peaks in the morning and evening[2]. Observations on Rhum show that most hinds mate with a single stag within each rut[2].

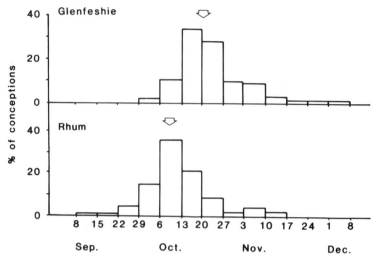

Figure 3.5   Distribution of conception dates at Glenfeshie and on Rhum, 1968-70.
The arrows indicate the medians: Glenfeshie – 19th October; Rhum – 9th October[15].

The timing of breeding in hinds is controlled by day-length but is also affected by the animal's weight and condition (see Section 3.6) as well as by the activities of rutting stags[18]. In the southern hemisphere the timing of breeding is displaced by six months but, within each hemisphere, there is no evidence that conception dates vary with latitude[19]. In Scotland, it is often suggested that conception dates are later in the central and eastern Highlands than on the west coast and the average date of conception is around ten days later at Glenfeshie than on Rhum[15] (see Figure 3.5). However, conception dates change with population density (see Chapter 5) and it is not yet clear whether they are consistently earlier on the west coast.

Few stags are able to hold a harem during the entire rut. From the beginning of September onwards, stags feed little and their body weight begins to fall rapidly (Figure 3.3). Mature stags lose as much as 20% of their body weight and over 80% of their body fat during the rut. The first stags begin to lose interest in their harems in the middle of the month and only a few rut actively for more than three weeks[11].

The gestation length of hinds is approximately 33 weeks[16,20]. Comparisons with other mammals suggest that although gestation length can be affected by environmental influences, it can seldom be changed by more than a few days[21]. Both resorption and fetal loss appear to be uncommon in red deer and evidence from other cervids

Plate 3.5   A newly born calf lying hidden in long grass. For the first week or two of life, calves are kept hidden, usually in long vegetation, their mothers visiting them several times a day to feed them. (Photograph: Fiona Guinness.)

suggests that the rate of foetal loss rarely exceeds 15%[22,23,24].

Most calves are born in June though occasional births occur into August and September or even October[2]. The first sign that a hind is about to calve is a swelling of the udder, usually one or two days before she gives birth. On Rhum, hinds about to calve move away from their usual core areas and often keep their calves on high ground, visiting them several times a day[25] (see Plate 3.5). The average birth weight of calves in the North Block is approximately 6.5 kg (14 lbs) though stag calves are typically born around half a kilogram (1 lb) heavier than females[26]. Calf birth weights vary widely between years (see Chapter 5) as well as between individual mothers. Small hinds consistently produce calves with birth weights of 4-5 kg while heavy animals produce calves of 7-8 kg[27,28]. In addition, larger, more dominant hinds produce a higher proportion of male calves than smaller, subordinate ones[4].

3.4   CALF SURVIVAL

Accurate measures of calf survival in wild red deer are only available from our study area in the North Block of Rhum. There, approximately a fifth of all calves born die in their first summer, mostly in the first five days of life[29]. As we describe in Chapter 5, neither neonatal mortality nor calf birth weights have changed with increasing population density. Calves born below average weight are more likely to die than heavier calves and late-born calves are more likely to die than those born during the peak of calving in mid-June. Common proximate causes of death include failure of the mother's milk supply, exposure, predation by eagles or gulls and drowning[29] (see Plate 3.6 (a), (b)).

Most calves that survive their first weeks of life live for at least six months[29]. Subsequently, mortality peaks in March and April at the end of their first and second winters. On Rhum, the proportion of calves that die in their first winter varies widely in response to changes in weather and population density. Even at this stage, the calf's early development exerts an important influence on its

Plate 3.6 (a)

Plate 3.6   Calf mortality on Rhum. (a) A four-day-old calf recently killed by an eagle. Eagles tend to remove internal organs and some flesh from the shoulder or haunch but seldom remove the eyes, which are the first part to be taken by hooded crows or gulls. (Photograph: Fiona Guinness.) (b) On Rhum, several weak calves have slipped and drowned while crossing burns. (Photograph: Fiona Guinness.)

survival. Calves that are born light or late are substantially more likely to die in winter than early- or heavy-born calves and this effect has increased as population density has risen (see Chapter 5). In addition, stag calves are more likely to die than hind calves, especially in high density populations (see Figure 5.7). Recent research on Rhum shows that genetic factors, too, are important and that a high proportion of calves carrying certain alleles die in their first two years of life[30].

3.5   GROWTH AND ANTLER DEVELOPMENT

The growth of calves slows at the onset of their first winter in response to changes in day-length and then virtually ceases until spring[22]. As fresh grass becomes available again in April and May, growth begins again but slows or ceases at the onset of each successive winter. Hinds can continue to grow until their fifth or

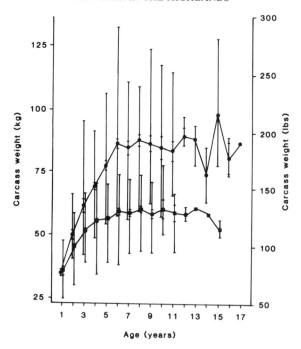

Figure 3.6 The age-specific weight of stags (●) and hinds (■) on Rhum[33]. Points show means, vertical lines the total ranges and standard error.

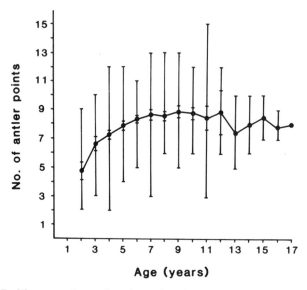

Figure 3.7 Mean numbers of antler points in relation to age in stags shot on Rhum[33]. Extending lines show total ranges and standard errors.

sixth year, stags until they are six or seven (Figure 3.6). In most areas of the Highlands, mature hind larder weights (carcase weight less bleedable blood, complete alimentary and reproductive tracts) probably lie between 40 and 65 kg (7 to 10 stone) while the larder weights of stags average between 75 and 100 kg (12 to 16 stone) (see Table 3.1). In stags, antler weight and point number usually increase until a stag is around seven or eight years old (see Figure 3.7).

The body size, weight and antler development of deer living on the open hill are all substantially lower than in most forest-living deer[35-38] or in farmed populations[22]. Much of this difference is caused by poor nutrition on the open hill, especially during early development. Experiments with captive deer show that hinds maintained on moorland pastures have milk yields 60% below those kept on improved grassland, and their calves show substantially lower growth rates[39]. Stag calves that are born light or are subjected to food shortage during their first winter are smaller than average as adults, despite compensatory growth the following summer[40] and their breeding success is probably low in most natural populations. Similarly, hinds born below average weight turn into small adults and, in their turn, produce light calves with a low chance of survival[27,28]. We describe the evidence for these relationships in more detail in Chapter 6.

There is some evidence that the weight of hinds and stags varies systematically across the Highlands. Between 1949 and 1959, Whitehead sent out questionnaires to all deer forest owners in Scotland asking, among other questions, for the average and maximum weights of hinds and stags killed on the estate. His book[41] gives average figures for 278 forests, widely distributed across the Highlands. These estimates have many limitations, among them the impossibility of correcting weights for differences in the timing of shooting within the season and, in addition, the fact that all of them were made over 25 years ago[42]. Analysis of average stag (larder) weights shows that this varies between deer forests from 76.4 to 110.9 kg while the larder weights of the heaviest stags recorded range from 101.8 to 194.5 kg. Average weights of hinds range from 36.7 to 82.7 kg.

Average stag weights tend to be higher in the south and western Highlands than in the north and east (Figure 3.8). This is probably a result of milder winters, for the average weights of stags are highest where January temperatures are also high: a 1°C increase in January temperature results in a 2.5 kg increase in larder weight[42]. At

Table 3.1 Measures of reproduction and performance in different Scottish deer forests. Figures in brackets indicate source references.

Measure year	Glen Dye 1965–1969 (3)	Invermark 1961–1965 (31)	Glenfeshie 1966–1974 (1,31,32)	Rhum 1957–1978 (8,33)	Scarba 1974–1975 (34)
Density (per km²)	3.4	15.3	13.1	13.9	34.43
Altitudinal range (m)	125–778	294–938	312–1265	0–812	0–448
x̄ January temperature	2.1	1.3	2.0	4.6	5.2
Annual rainfall (mm)	1050	1090	900	2500	1660
Adult sex ratio (hinds per 100 stags)	198	556	140	116	157
Calf/hind ratio in spring (calves per 100 hinds)	45.8	41.5	34.6	38.1	39.2
Percentage of yearlings pregnant	64*	43*	0	0	0
Yearling hind larder weight (kg)	42.6	40.4	38.0	37.0	37.2
Percentage of milk hinds pregnant	94	83	44	51	39
Milk hind larder weight (kg)†	54.7	51.7	46.5	51.0	58.9
Stag larder weight (kg)‡	78.6	92.1	83.8	88.7	93.7

*Based on small sample sizes.
†Milk hind larder weight 60% of live weight.
‡Stag larder weight 73% of live weight.

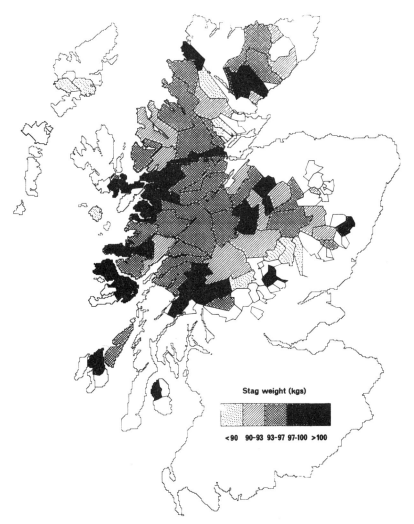

Figure 3.8 The distribution of average stag weights across Scotland. Data are from Whitehead[41] and were collected between 1949 and 1959. Estimates for estates have been combined to give a weighted mean (based on area of estate) for each parish.

Glenfeshie, for example, where the average January temperature is only 1.3°C (mean for 1966 to 1974), the average larder weight of seven year old stags is 85.0 kg whereas, on Rhum, where average temperatures in January are 4.5°C (1959-1978), average stag weights are 89.0 kg. Thus a 3.2°C difference in temperature is associated with a 4 kg difference in weight, a similar difference to that predicted by the overall trend across Scotland. Maximum stag weights follow the same trend. In contrast, the best predictor of hind weights is the availability of low ground[42]. For every increase of 100 m in the height of the lowest ground available to the deer, average hind weight falls by 1.5 kg. Hind weights and the availability of low ground are also positively correlated with annual rainfall and negatively with the number of days of snow cover each year.

Like body weight, antler development also appears to be related to individual differences in early development as well as to nutrition during adulthood. However, it is not yet clear to what extent genetic factors are important. While it would be surprising if there was not *some* effect of the father's genes on the antler growth of his sons, the available information suggests that this may be slight. Like many other animal weapons, antlers have a low growth priority[43] and their size is more strongly affected by food shortage and other environmental factors than other aspects of the stag's size. For example, deterioration of habitat or rising population density can produce a rapid decline in antler size[2,33].

Research on hummels (antlerless stags) supports the view that environmental factors exert a strong effect on antler development. In some parts of the Highlands, a proportion of stags (usually less than 1%) fail to produce antlers[44,45]. It is widely believed that hummels are heavier than antlered stags and can often displace them from harems during the rut[44]. Though they may occasionally do so, there is no evidence that their fighting success is superior to that of antlered stags. The two systematic attempts to compare the body weights of hummels and antlered stags found no differences in weight or size between them[45,46] (see Figure 3.9).

Breeding experiments with hummels show that the absence of antlers is not under simple genetic control[47-52]. By breeding from hummels caught at Braemar and Loch Choire in Sutherland, Lincoln was able to show that their sons grew normal antlers and that antler loss was not caused by a simple dominant gene. Subsequently, one of the hummels was back-crossed with his own daughters and stag calves produced by these matings again showed normal antler growth. The general conclusion of Lincoln and Fletcher's experiments is that many, if not all, hummels are individuals that never produced normal pedicles, possibly as a result of malnutrition in their first year or two of life[46].

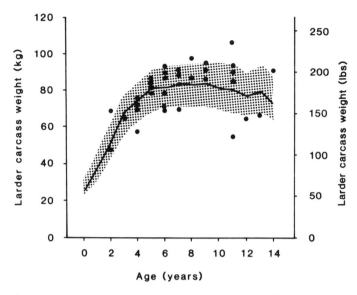

Figure 3.9 Carcase weights of 31 hummels compared with the average weight (solid line) and standard deviation (hatched area) of 1029 antlered stags shot at Glenfeshie.

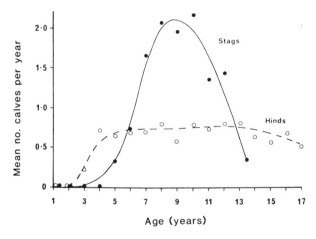

Figure 3.10 Reproductive success of stags and hinds at different ages in the North Block of Rhum.

3.6 REPRODUCTIVE PERFORMANCE AND AGE

In mammals, almost all biological processes change as an animal matures and then ages, including the ability to locate and assimilate food, the rate of weight gain in spring and summer and weight loss

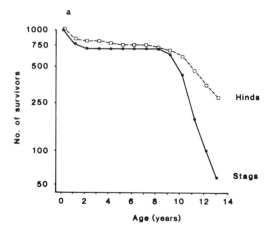

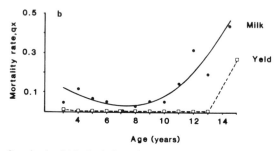

Figure 3.11 Survival of hinds (□) and stags (●) in an unculled population on Rhum[from 28]. The lower plot shows the proportion of milk (●) versus yeld hinds (□) dying at each age[28,60].

in winter and almost all aspects of reproductive performance and survival. The management of mammal populations depends on an accurate knowledge of these processes.

Accurate estimates of changes in reproduction and survival with age were unavailable before the 1950s. When Fraser Darling carried out his study of red deer at Dundonell[44], he had no firm basis for aging individuals and his book tells us surprisingly little about their reproductive performance or life histories. A major advance was the development of accurate aging techniques, based on annual growth layers in cement of molar teeth[53,54]. Independently, a reliable method for aging deer based on the eruption, replacement and wear of molar teeth was developed from known-aged jaws[55]. These methods were used to establish the effects of age on reproductive success and survival[1,32].

In both sexes, autumn body weight declines towards the end of the

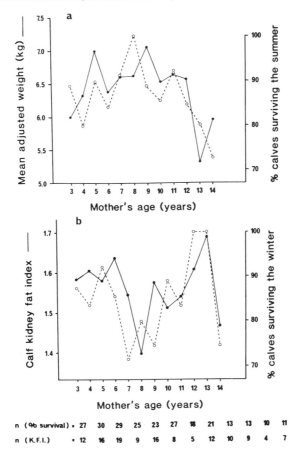

Figure 3.12   (a) Birth weights (adjusted for sex of calf and year of birth) of calves born to mothers of different ages in the North Block of Rhum, 1971–79 (solid line). The proportion of calves in each category that survived till October is also shown (broken line)[from 56]; (b) The proportion of calves born to mothers of different ages in the North Block of Rhum that survived their first winter (broken line). The plots show data collected 1971–79 and exclude all calves dying before their first October. Mean kidney fat indices of calves born to mothers of different ages shot between November and February in Glenfeshie are also shown (solid line). Sample sizes are shown below each plot[from 56].

lifespan though this change is not pronounced. Body condition (as measured by the kidney fat index) declines throughout the lifespan in milk hinds and after the age of ten or eleven in stags[1].

In stags, fighting success, harem size and mating success usually drop off rapidly after an animal passes its tenth year (Figure 3.10). Occasionally, stags continue to rut successfully until they are twelve or thirteen, but this is unusual and reports of much older stags

Plate 3.7 (a) On coastal forests, like Rhum, stags feeding on the tide line often pick up lengths of fishing net on their antlers. This can enmesh and later kill them. (Photograph: Fiona Guinness.) (b) Early spring mortality: a hind, her yearling and calf, which have died as a group. Food shortage in winter combined with rainfall and wind in March and April is one of the commonest causes of death in Highland deer. (Photograph: Lea MacNally.)

continuing to breed are likely to be cases of mistaken identity, for the survival of stags declines sharply after they pass the age of nine (see Figure 3.11(a)).

In hinds, the decline in reproductive performance occurs later and is less pronounced. On Rhum, fecundity does not begin to fall until hinds pass their twelfth year and then only in milk hinds (see Chapter 5). The birth weight and over-summer survival of their calves declines at the same time (Figure 3.12a). However, these trends may be partly compensated for by an *increase* in the over-winter survival of calves born to old hinds (Figure 3.12b). Old and young mothers appear to suckle their calves for longer and evidence both from Rhum and from Glenfeshie suggests that their offspring are in better conditon and are more likely to live through their first winter than those of middle-aged hinds[56]. As a result, the decline in production of surviving calves with increasing age is relatively slight (Figure 3.10).

The survival of hinds begins to decline after they pass their tenth year. Hinds are substantially more likely to die in years when they are rearing calves than when they are yeld (Figure 3.11(b)) (see Plate 3.7).

3.7   THE COSTS OF BREEDING

The energetic costs to the mother of gestation and, especially, lactation are high. Calves take between 200 and 600 g of milk per feed and the milk yields of hinds can be as high as 2000 g per day[57]. The total food requirements of milk hinds during the peak of lactation in late June and July are estimated to be about twice as high as those of yeld hinds[58]. Unlike yeld hinds, mothers that are rearing calves show little gain in body weight or condition during the summer (Figure 3.13). However, yeld hinds lose weight rapidly during the winter while milk hinds appear to maintain a lower but approximately constant weight[8].

The lower weight and poorer body condition of milk hinds affects their fecundity. Both on Rhum and at Glenfeshie, over 90% of yeld hinds conceive in the rut while the proportion of milk hinds conceiving is often much lower (see Chapters 5 and 6). The extent of this difference depends on the density of the population and the availability of food and, in some populations, the proportion of milk hinds conceiving can fall as low as 30%[2]. In addition, milk hinds

Plate 3.8   Stripping the skin from a stag in good condition during the autumn cull.
Note the substantial deposits of fat on the rump and above the rib cage. By the end
of the rut, stags have usually exhausted their reserves. (Photograph: Lea
MacNally.)

conceive around a week later than yeld hinds[2,15,32]. These effects are
restricted to mothers that raise a calf into the winter months: hinds
that produce a calf but lose it shortly after birth gain weight in the
rest of the summer and their fecundity is nearly as high as that of
hinds that do not conceive[2].

Surprisingly, there is no difference in the birth weight of calves
born to milk and yeld hinds nor is there any firm evidence that, as is
sometimes suggested, yeld hinds are more likely to produce stag
calves[2,4]. The calves of yeld hinds do not suckle longer or more
frequently than those of milk hinds and they are more, and not less,
likely to die during their first year of life. Of samples of 245 and 166
calves born to milk and yeld hinds in our study area on Rhum, 27%
of the calves of milk hinds died in their first twelve months,

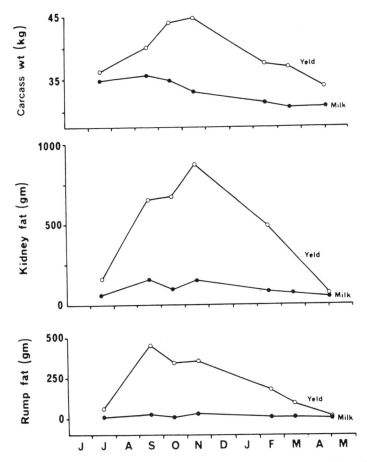

Figure 3.13 Changes in carcase weight, kidney fat, and rumpfat in milk and yeld hinds shot throughout the year on Rhum[from 8].

compared to 38% of those belonging to mature yeld hinds[60]. The likely reason for this surprising trend is that aspects of the mother's physique or environment that reduce her chances of rearing a calf successfully in one year (such as small body size, low social rank or a poor-quality home range) operate in successive years. Comparison of the performance of the same hinds in successive years showed that mothers did produce heavier calves after they had been yeld the previous year. However, the superior body condition of yeld hinds during the summer has relatively little effect on calf growth and survival since it is mostly lost during the course of the winter (Figure 3.13).

3.8   IMPLICATIONS FOR MANAGEMENT

These results provide some indication of the categories of animals that should be selectively culled if the aim of management is to maximize production and performance. In particular, they confirm the value of culling mature yeld hinds. It is sometimes argued that, since yeld hinds are in superior condition to milk hinds at the beginning of the winter, they are likely to produce the best calves the following season and so should be spared[61]. Our results from Rhum show that although individuals show superior reproductive performance after they have been yeld the previous year, overall the calves of mature yeld hinds are no heavier at birth than those of milk hinds and they are more, not less, likely to die in their first year of life. This presumably occurs because the same factors that predispose a hind to lose her calf in one year are also likely to affect the survival of her subsequent calves.

Some estates selectively cull older hinds in order to minimize natural mortality. However, the available information suggests that the survival of hinds does not decline until they reach 12-13 years and their effective reproductive rate does not fall off until the same age (Figure 3.10). In a culled population, only a small proportion of animals will reach this age and the effects of selective culling may therefore be small. There are, in addition, two arguments against consistent selection of (apparently) older hinds. First, animals that appear old often include the best and most productive mothers, whose condition in winter is low as a result of their investment in their calves. And secondly, evidence from other mammals that live in matrilineal groups suggests that the removal of matriarchs often leads to the aggregation of neighbouring groups into large herds. If this occurs in red deer, not only may it make culling harder but, as we describe in Chapter 5, increasing group size is likely to be associated with a reduction in reproductive performance. In general, it is probably sensible to cull old yeld hinds and old milk hinds with poor calves but to spare those animals with well-grown calves whatever their apparent age.

One aspect of hind culling which has not been adequately stressed is the need to distribute culls evenly in relation to population density. The available evidence suggests that hinds are reluctant to disperse from their natal area and that groups are slow to shift their range (see above and Chapter 4). The concentration of hind culls in particular areas is likely to reduce population density in those sites and to have little influence on hinds in neighbouring areas. As

Osborne demonstrated, effects of this kind may possibly lower potential yields by more than 25%[62]. In addition, it is important to ensure that approximately the same *proportion* of hinds are taken from different areas. On ground where hind numbers are low, removal of the same *number* of hinds per unit area of ground may rapidly extinguish the local population, leaving a gap that other groups may be slow to fill.

Many Highland estates follow the practice of selectively culling stags with small or irregular antlers and sparing animals with good heads in the hope that this will help to improve antler growth in future generations. Since the extent to which antler size and shape are inherited is unknown, it is impossible to predict how effective this policy is likely to be. The extensive evidence that antler size is strongly influenced by environmental factors (see Chapter 5), suggests that the heritability of antler size may be low and, if so, selective shooting may have little effect. Though it is sometimes argued that selective shooting has improved the quality of heads on particular forests, none of these claims has yet been backed up by measurements. It is, of course, very easy to gain a false impression that the quality of antlers is responding to selective culling since the removal of stags with poor antlers leads, inevitably, to an increase in the average antler size of survivors. However, this need not, of course, indicate that the *average quality of the heads produced by the next generation* is improving.

Finally, the tendency in stags on at least some estates to disperse from their natal area may have far-reaching implications for management policies. As we describe in Section 3.2, two forms of dispersal occur: the temporary dispersal of mature stags from their summer or winter ranges to their rutting grounds in September and October; and the permanent dispersal of young stags from the area where they are born to winter or summer ranges in other localities. The first of these two processes is reasonably well documented and individual stags can move considerable distances. The permanent dispersal of young stags from their natal areas has yet to be investigated in mainland red deer, but it is common on Rhum and male dispersal is a feature of most mammals[7]. In some areas of the Highlands, the situation may be further complicated by dispersal of stags to forestry or woodland.

The importance of both forms of dispersal is that all deer forests are likely to lose a proportion of the stags born on their ground either through the temporary dispersal of mature animals in the rut or as a result of permanent dispersal of stags between the ages of two and five. Overall, losses through emigration will be offset by gains through immigration, but some forests are likely to be net gainers and others net losers through both processes. In the case of smaller deer forests the relative rates of emigration and immigration may be one of the most important determinants of the number of stags that can be killed each year. However, virtually nothing is known of the factors that affect the rate of dispersal (see Chapter 5).

3.9 SUMMARY

3.1 The population ecology of red deer living on the open hill has been investigated in detail on Rhum, off the west coast, and at Glenfeshie in the eastern Highlands. Shorter studies have also been carried out at Glen Fiddich, Invermark, Glen Lui, Glen Tanar, Glen Dye and Ben Lawers as well as in Wester Ross and South Ross and on the islands of Jura and Scarba.

3.2 A hind's daughters usually adopt home ranges overlapping that of their mother and associate with related animals throughout their lives. In contrast, stags form looser groups. A proportion of stags disperse from their natal area between the age of two and five. In addition, rutting stags commonly disperse temporarily from their summer range to spend the breeding season in other areas.

3.3 Around 80% of all calves are conceived in October. The timing of breeding in hinds is controlled by daylength but is also influenced by their weight and condition as well as by the activities of stags. Calves are born approximately thirty-three weeks after conception, mostly in the second and third weeks of June.

3.4 On Rhum, between 10 and 20% of all calves die in their first summer and a further 5 – 40% die at the end of their first winter. Light and late-born calves are particularly likely to die and genetic factors, too, may be important.

3.5 The abundance and quality of food available to hinds has a pronounced effect on their milk yield as well as on the birth weight and growth of their calves. Early growth, in turn, affects body size and reproductive performance in adulthood. The antler size of stags is also strongly influenced by nutrition and environmental factors operating during development.

3.6 Both in stags and hinds, age exerts a strong influence on survival and reproductive performance. These effects are particularly strong in stags, whose breeding success and survival decline after they reach the age of ten. In hinds, they are later and less pronounced and the breeding success of hinds shows little decline until they are over twelve.

3.7 Fecundity is consistently higher in mature yeld hinds than in milk hinds due to their superior body condition. However, mature yeld hinds are less likely to rear their calves successfully than milk hinds.

3.8   These results support the common practice of selectively culling mature yeld hinds. They also emphasize the need for hind culls to be evenly distributed across the population. At the moment, it is not clear to what extent antler size and shape are affected by genetic characteristics and the effects of selectively shooting stags with good or poor heads are unknown.

The higher rates of disperal by stags (either temporarily to their rutting grounds or permanently to new home ranges) suggest that the relative rates of immigration and emigration may be one of the most important determinants of the number of stags that a deer forest can kill, but virtually nothing is known of the factors affecting these processes.

REFERENCES

1. Mitchell, B., Staines, B. W. & Welch, D. (1977). *Ecology of Red Deer: a Research Review Relevant to their Management.* Inst. of Terrestrial Ecology, Cambridge.

2. Clutton-Brock, T. H., Guinness, F. E. & Albon, S. D. (1982). *Red Deer: Behavior and Ecology of Two Sexes.* University of Chicago Press, Chicago.

3. Clutton-Brock, T. H., Albon, S. D. & Guinness, F. E. (1982). 'Competition between female relatives in a matrilocal mammal'. *Nature,* **300,** 178-180.

4. Clutton-Brock, T. H., Albon, S. D. & Guinness, F. E. (1986). 'Great expectations: dominance, breeding success and offspring sex ratios in red deer'. *Anim. Behav.,* **34,** 460-471.

5. Appleby, M. C. (1983). 'Competition in a red deer stag group: rank, age and relatedness of opponents'. *Anim. Behav.,* **31,** 913-918.

6. *Red Deer Commission Annual Report* (1983–1985). H.M.S.O., Edinburgh.

7. Greenwood, P. (1980). 'Mating systems, philopatry and dispersal in birds and mammals'. *Anim. Behav.,* **28,**1140-62.

8. Mitchell, B., McCowan, D. & Nicholson, I. A. (1976). 'Annual cycles of body weight and condition in Scottish red deer, *Cervus elaphus'. J. Zool. Lond.,* **180,** 107-127.

9. Lincoln, G. A. (1971a). 'The seasonal reproductive changes in the red deer stag (*Cervus elaphus*)'. *J. Zool. Lond.,* **163,** 105-123.

10. Lincoln, G. A., Youngson, R. W. & Short, R. V. (1970). 'The social and sexual behaviour of the red deer stag'. *J. Reprod. Fert. Suppl.,* **11,** 71-103.

11. Clutton-Brock, T. H., Albon, S. D., Gibson, R. M. & Guinness, F. E. (1979). 'The logical stag: adaptive aspects of fighting in red deer

(*Cervus elaphus* L.)'. *Anim. Behav.,* **27**, 211–225.

12. Clutton-Brock, T. H. (1982). 'The functions of antlers'. *Behaviour,* **79**, 108–125.

13. Lincoln, G. A. (1972). 'The role of antlers in the behaviour of red deer'. *J. Exp. Zool.,* **182**, 233–250.

14. Clutton-Brock, T. H. (1985). 'Reproductive success in red deer'. *Scientific American,* **252**, 86–92.

15. Mitchell, B. & Lincoln, G. A. (1973). 'Conception dates in relation to age and condition in two populations of red deer in Scotland'. *J. Zool.,* **171**, 141–152.

16. Guinness, F. E., Lincoln, G. A. & Short, R. V. (1971). 'The reproductive cycle of the female red deer, *Cervus elaphus* L'. *J. Reprod. Fert.,* **27**, 427–438.

17. Iason, G. R. & Guinness, F. E. (1985). 'Synchrony of oestrus and conception in red deer (*Cervus elaphus* L.)'. *Anim. Behav.,* **33**, 1169–1174.

18. McComb, K. (1987). *Roaring by Red Deer Advances: The Date of Oestrus in Hinds.* Nature, **330**, 648–649.

19. Fletcher, T. J. (1974). 'The timing of reproduction in red deer (*Cervus elaphus*) in relation to latitude'. *J. Zool.,* **172**, 363–367.

20. Guinness, F. E., Gibson, R. M. & Clutton-Brock, T. H. (1978). 'Calving times in red deer (*Cervus elaphus*) on Rhum'. *J. Zool.,* **185**, 105–114.

21. Racey, P. A. (1981). 'Environmental factors affecting gestation lengths in mammals'. In: *Environmental Factors in Mammal Reproduction* pp. 197–213. eds. D. Gilmore & B. Cook. Macmillan, London.

22. Blaxter, K. L., Kay, R. N. B., Sharman, G. A. M., Cunningham, J. M. M. & Hamilton, W. J. (1974). *Farming the Red Deer.* H.M.S.O., London.

23. Staines, B. (1978). 'The dynamics and performance of a declining population of red deer (*Cervus elaphus*)'. *J. Zool. Lond.,* **184**, 403–419.

24. Thorne, E. T., Dean, R. E. & Hepworth, W. G. (1976). 'Nutrition during gestation in relation to sucessful reproduction in elk'. *J. Wildl. Mgmt.,* **40**, 330–335.

25. Clutton-Brock, T. H. & Guinness, F. E. (1975). 'Behaviour of red deer (*Cervus elaphus* L.) at calving time'. *Behaviour,* **55**, 287–300.

26. Albon, S. D., Guinness, F. E. & Clutton-Brock, T. H. (1983). 'The influence of climatic variation on the birth weights of red deer (*Cervus elaphus*)'. *J. Zool.,* **200**, 295–298.

27. Albon, S. D., Clutton-Brock, T. H. & Guinness, F. E. (1987). 'Early development and population dynamics in red deer II. Density-independent effects and cohort variation'. *J. Anim. Ecol.,* **56**, 69–82.

28. Clutton-Brock, T. H., Albon, S. D. & Guinness, F. E. (1988). 'Reproductive success in male and female red deer'. In: *Reproductive Success*, ed. T. H. Clutton-Brock, pp. 325–343. University of Chicago Press, Chicago.

29. Guinness, F. E., Clutton-Brock, T. H. & Albon, S. D. (1978). 'Factors affecting calf mortality in red deer'. *J. Anim. Ecol.,* **47**, 812–832.

30. Pemberton, J., Albon, S. D., Guinness, F. E., Clutton-Brock, T. H. & Berry, R. J. (1988). 'Genetic variation and juvenile survival in red deer'. *Evolution,* **42**, 921–934.

31. Mitchell, B. (1973). 'The reproductive performance of wild Scottish red deer *Cervus elaphus*'. *J. Reprod. Fert. Suppl.,* **19**, 271–285.

32. Mitchell, B., McCowan, D. & Parish, T. (1986). 'Performance and population dynamics in relation to management of red deer *Cervus elaphus* at Glenfeshie, Inverness-shire, Scotland'. *Biological Conservation,* **37**, 237–267.

33. Lowe, V. P. W. (1971). 'Some effects of a change in estate management on a deer population'. In: *The Scientific Management of Animal and Plant Communities for Conservation*, ed. Duffey, E. & Watt, A. S., pp. 437–445. Blackwell Scientific Publications, Oxford.

34. Mitchell, B. & Crisp, J. M. (1981). 'Some properties of red deer (*Cervus elaphus*) at exceptionally high population density in Scotland'. *J. Zool.,* **193**, 157–169.

35. Mitchell, B., Grant, W. & Cubby, J. (1981). 'Notes on the performance of red deer *Cervus elaphus* in a woodland habitat'. *J. Zool. Lond.,* **194**, 279–284.

36. Ratcliffe, P. R. (1984a). 'Population dynamics of red deer (*Cervus elaphus* L.) in Scottish commercial forests'. *Proc. Roy. Soc. Edinb.,* **82B**, 291–302.

37. Ratcliffe, P. R. (1984b). 'Population density and reproduction of red deer in Scottish commercial forests'. *Acta Zool. Fenn.* **172**, 191–192.

38. Ratcliffe, P. R. (1987). 'Red deer population changes in woodland and the independent assessment of population size'. In: *Mammal Population Studies*, ed. S. Harris. Symp. Zoological Society, Lond., **58**, 153–165.

39. Loudon, A. S. I., Darroch, A. & Milne, J. A. (1984). 'The lactation performance of red deer on hill and improved species pastures'. *J. Agric. Sci.,* Cambridge, **102**, 149–158.

40. Suttie, J. M., Goodall, E. D., Pennie, K. & Kay, R. N. B. (1983). 'Winter feed restriction and summer compensation in red deer stags (*Cervus elaphus*)'. *Brit. J. Nutr.,* **50**, 737–747.

41. Whitehead, G. K. (1960). *The Deerstalking Grounds of Great Britain and Ireland*. Hollis & Carter, London.

42. Watts, A. (1980). 'Spatial variation in the performance of Scottish red

deer'. Diploma thesis, Department of Statistics, University of Cambridge.

43. Huxley, J. S. (1932). *Problems of Relative Growth*. MacVeagh, London.

44. Darling, F. F. (1937). *A Herd of Red Deer*. O.U.P., London.

45. Mitchell, B. & Parish, T. (1970). 'Are hummels bigger than stags with normal antlers?' *Deer,* **2**, 521–522.

46. Lincoln, G. & Fletcher, T. (1984). 'History of a hummel Part VII. Nature vs. nurture'. *Deer,* **6**, 127–131.

47. Lincoln, G. (1969). 'History of a hummel 1'. *Deer,* **1**, 327–328.

48. Lincoln, G. (1970). 'History of a hummel 2'. *Deer,* **2**, 630–632.

49. Lincoln, G. (1973). 'History of a hummel 3'. *Deer,* **3**, 26–27.

50. Lincoln, G. (1976). 'History of a hummel 4'. *Deer,* **3**, 552–553.

51. Lincoln, G. (1977). 'History of a hummel 5'. *Deer,* **4**, 86–87.

52. Lincoln, G. (1978). 'History of a hummel 6'. *Deer,* **4**, 274–275.

53. Mitchell, B. (1963). 'Determination of age in Scottish red deer from growth layers in dental cement'. *Nature,* **198**, 350–351.

54. Mitchell, B. (1967). 'Growth layers in dental cement for determining the age of red deer (*Cervus elaphus* L.)'. *J. Anim. Ecol.,* **36**, 279–293.

55. Lowe, V. P. W. (1967). 'Teeth as indicators of age with special reference to red deer of known age from Rhum'. *J. Zool.,* **152**, 137–153.

56. Clutton-Brock, T. H. (1984). 'Reproductive effort and terminal investment in iteroparous animals'. *Am. Nat.,* **123**, 212–229.

57. Arman, P., Kay, R. N. B., Goodall, E. D. & Sharman, G. A. M. (1974). 'The composition and yield of milk from captive red deer (*Cervus elaphus* L.)'. *J. Reprod. Fert.,* **37**, 67–84.

58. Anderson, J. E. M. (1976). 'Food energy requirements of wild Scottish red deer'. In: *The Red Deer in South Ross*, ed. W. E. S. Mutch, J. D. Lockie & A. S. Cooper, Dept. Forestry and Natural Resources, University of Edinburgh.

59. Clutton-Brock, T. H., Albon, S. D. & Guinness, F. E. (1981). 'Parental investment in male and female offspring in polygynous mammals'. *Nature,* **289**, 487–489.

60. Clutton-Brock, T. H., Guinness, F. E. & Albon, S. D. (1983). 'The costs of reproduction to red deer hinds'. *J. Anim. Ecol.,* **52**, 367–384.

61. Mutch, W. E. S., Lockie, J. D. & Cooper, A. N. (1976). *The Red Deer in South Ross: a Report on Wildlife Management in the Scottish Highlands*. Department of Forestry & Natural Resources, University of Edinburgh.

62. Osborne, B. C. (1980). 'The grazing ecology and management of red deer and hill sheep on Ardtornish Estate', Argyll. M. Phil. thesis, University of Sussex.

4 Feeding Behaviour and Habitat Use

4.1 INTRODUCTION

In this chapter, we describe the feeding behaviour of Highland red deer throughout the year (Section 4.2), their diet and use of habitat (Sections 4.3 and 4.4) and their impact on the plant communities that they use (Section 4.5). In Sections 4.6 and 4.7 we outline what is known of the effects of two common management practices, burning upland vegetation (muirburn) and supplementary feeding, while in Section 4.8 we describe studies of ecological interactions between red deer and domestic stock. Finally, in the last section we discuss the management implications of the studies of red deer feeding and habitat manipulation.

The diet or habitat use of red deer has been investigated in detail in seven areas: at Glen Dye[1,2] and at several sites around Deeside in the Eastern Highlands[3-7]; at Glenfeshie, in the Central Highlands[8,9]; near Killin, in the Southern Highlands[10]; at Glen Goibhre in Ross-shire[11]; at Ardtornish, in Argyll[12]; and on Rhum, in the Inner Hebrides[13-18] (Figure 1.1). In addition, research at the Rowett Research Institute near Aberdeen and at the Hill Farming Research Organisation's deer farm at Glensaugh in Kincardineshire has examined their digestive physiology and appetite[19-22].

The diet of red deer varies widely throughout the Highlands in response to differences in the plant communities they live on. The main range of red deer in the Highlands can be divided into two zones based on rainfall and soil type[23]. A line from the north coast of Sutherland, running southward and continuing through Newtonmore, marks the division between the two types of environment. To the north and west of this, rainfall is high, soils are usually peaty (mor) and swards are dominated by purple moor grass (*Molinia caerulea*), deer sedge, (*Trichophorum cespitosum*), bog cotton (*Eriophorum vaginatum*) and bilberry (*Vaccinium myrtillus*) with variable amounts of heather. To the south and east, rainfall is lower, sandy, mineralized (mull) soils are more common (though they are frequently covered by peaty humus) and heather (*Calluna vulgaris*) predominates, interspersed with areas of relatively palatable grassland[24].

Despite pronounced variation in vegetation throughout the Highlands, almost all areas used by red deer share three important characteristics. First, most of the available vegetation is unacceptable to the deer for most of the year because its fibre or lignin content is high and its digestibility is extremely low (Table 4.1).

Table 4.1　Digestibilities of common upland plants. Figures show the *in vitro* percentage of dry matter digestibilities, usually using sheep liquor (from[22]).

	Spring	Summer	Autumn	Winter
Grasses				
Deschampsia flexuosa	75	57–68	77	62–69
Festuca rubra	75	57–68	72–73	48–63
Holcus mollus	76	62–72	69–73	42–53
Agrostis tenuis	76	62–72	64–70	35–41
Molinia caerulea	67	47–65	50	–
Agrostis/Festuca grassland	32–44	47–65	50	–
Sedges				
Eriophorum vaginatum	62	37–49	39	43
Trichophorum cespitosum	67	58–64	40	–
Carex spp.	67	58–64	56	54
Drawf shrubs and trees				
Calluna vulgaris	60	44–52	–	–
(Mature)	–	41–42	–	–
(Mature)	29–31	–	24	27
(Mature)	–	–	45	–
(Pioneer)	–	47	–	–
(Building)	–	46–48	46	42
(Mature)	–	49	–	–
Juniperus communis	41–43	–	38	43
Betula spp.	27–34	–	25	29

Especially in the north and west of the Highlands, deer are usually exploiting small areas of preferred swards, often characterised by the presence of bents (*Agrostis* spp.) and fescues (*Festuca* spp.), in a large expanse of unpalatable vegetation. Moreover, because Highland red deer subsist largely on moorland grasses and heather growing on heavily leached peat and acid soils, their food supply is often deficient or unbalanced in many major and trace minerals[22].

Second, the availability of live grasses used by the deer is strongly seasonal, showing a peak between July and September depending on altitude, followed by a rapid decline (see Figure 4.1). Throughout most of the Highlands, over 75% of grass growth occurs during a six week period in mid-summer. Perennial grasses either show little growth in winter or cease growing entirely and the availability of live vegetation is usually low. In contrast, heather does not die back totally and provides live matter throughout the year, except after particularly severe winter frosts[25-27].

Third, the quality and duration of growing seasons vary between years, depending on seasonal differences in temperature and rainfall. In spring appreciable grass growth does not begin until the

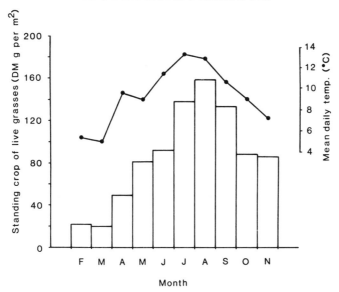

Figure 4.1   Standing crop of live grasses on *Agrostis-Festuca* swards in the North Block of Rhum in each month between February and November 1984. Mean daily temperature on Rhum is shown for the same months.

temperature rises above 6°C and ceases when it falls below this level again, the interval between being defined as the growing season[28]. On Rhum, with its moist, mild climate, the mean onset of the growing season between 1959 and 1980 was 5 March and the mean duration 282 days, while at Glenfeshie, with its more continental climate, the mean onset of the growing season between 1966 and 1974 was 25 April and the mean duration only 184 days[29]. The duration of the growing season was more variable on Rhum (range 236–365 days) with the mean monthly temperature never dropping below 6°C in some winters and some grass growth continuing.

Variation in summer rainfall is important, too. High rainfall early in the summer accelerates production in many grasses and sedges, increasing the abundance of food available to the deer. However, high rainfall in late summer, particularly in September, is commonly associated with lower surface temperatures, an early cessation of growth[30] and low food availability at the beginning of the winter (Figure 4.2). In contrast to most grasses, heather grows best in warm, dry summers (Figure 4.3). In eastern Scotland the abundance of new shoots, an important winter food[9], declines in years when the summer months are cool and wet[31].

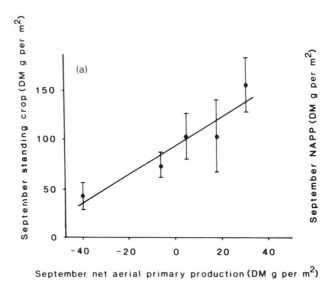

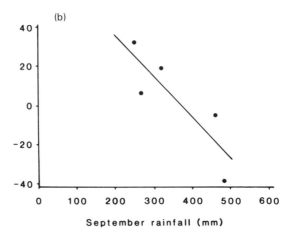

Figure 4.2 (a) September standing crop (DM g per m^2) of live grasses and herbs plotted against net aerial primary production (NAPP) (DM g per m^2) in September measured on *Agrostis-Festuca* vegetation communities in the North Block of Rhum between 1981 and 1985. Each point is mean of six plots. Bars show ±1 S.D. (b) September net aerial primary production (NAPP) (DM g per m^2) measured on *Agrostis-Festuca* vegetation communities in the North Block of Rhum plotted against rainfall in the same month each year between 1981 and 1985.

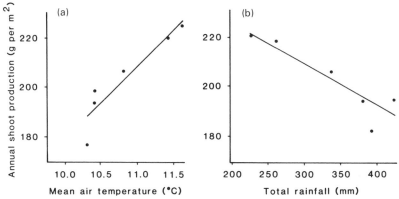

Figure 4.3 Annual shoot production by heather plotted against (a) mean daily air temperature (°C) and (b) rainfall between mid-April and August for six years[31]. In each graph the annual shoot production has been adjusted for the variation due to the other independent variable.

4.2 FEEDING BEHAVIOUR AND APPETITE

Like most ruminants, Highland red deer feed throughout the twenty-four hours. The ten to twelve hours they spend feeding per day is divided into six to ten bouts of grazing, usually lasting between one and two hours and interspersed with periods of rumination or resting[16]. Continuous watches of individuals throughout the twenty-four hours in the North Block of Rhum show that grazing peaks occur between 16.00 and 20.00 in both summer and winter (see Figure 4.4) and that less time is spent grazing at night than in the day. On many mainland forests, increased human disturbance of low ground is probably associated with a relative increase in night-time grazing. In winter, when food availability and quality are low, grazing and ruminating time increases and the deer maintain higher levels of rumen-fill and gut-fill[8,16,22].

The appetite of red deer stags varies seasonally. Even in the absence of hinds, the food intake of captive stags falls by around 40% between September and December, rising in January and February to a peak between March and June[20,21]. Changes in appetite are triggered by changes in day length and are presumably under hormonal control for the intake of castrated stags varies less than that of intact animals (see Figure 4.5). They are sufficient to produce substantial weight loss in mature stags and a growth check in young animals, though this is less pronounced in calves[21]. It is not yet clear whether the reduction in appetite in autumn and winter

(a) Summer

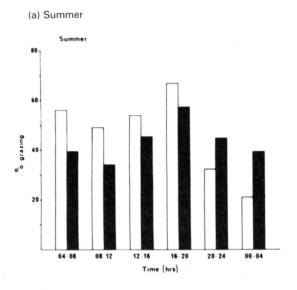

(b) Winter

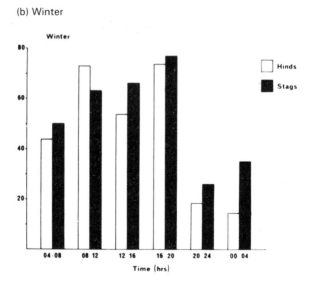

Figure 4.4   Mean percentage of time spent grazing during different periods of the day by hinds (□) and stags (■) in (a) summer and (b) winter on Rhum[16].

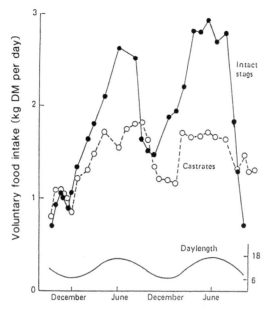

Figure 4.5 Voluntary intake of pelleted concentrate by intact (●) or castrate (o) stags, kept in pens with natural lighting[from 20].

is an adaptation to the normal reproductive activity of stags or to the low availability of food in winter: the fact that their appetite reaches its highest levels in March and April when food availability is at its lowest (see Figure 4.5) suggests that it may be an adaptation to the normal reduction in food intake during the rut.

4.3   DIET AND HABITAT USE

Analysis of plant fragments from the rumens of shot animals or from faeces show that broad-leaved grasses, especially bents (*Agrostis*), narrow leaved grasses, including fescues (*Festuca*) and *Deschampsia flexuosa*, together with heathers (mostly *Calluna vulgaris*) make up around 90% of the deers' diet in most areas of the Highlands (see Figure 4.6, Plate 4.1). On west coast deer forests, like Rhum, broad-leaved grasses are more abundant than in the eastern and southern Highlands while narrow-leaved grasses show an opposite trend[23]. Grasses of both kinds are most heavily used in spring and summer.

   In the eastern Highlands, heather is more abundant and provides a higher proportion of the diet than on the west coast, in some areas

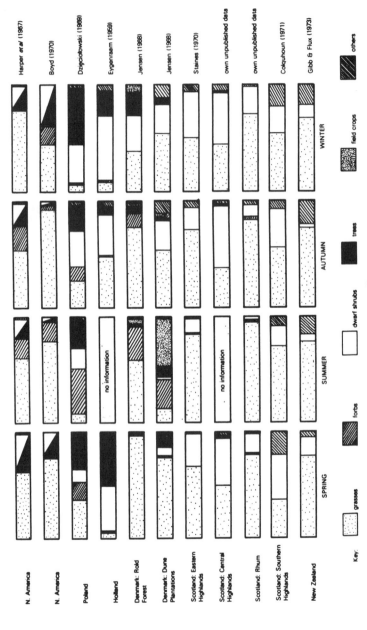

Figure 4.6 Foods eaten by red deer in different populations[8]. The works on North American Wapiti did not differentiate between browsing on trees and dwarf shrubs.

Plate 4.1   A nine year old stag on Rhum feeds on *Agrostis/Festuca* greens in his normal home range shortly after his return from the rut. His belly has already filled out since his return. (Photograph: Fiona Guinness.)

making up nearly 50% of the animal's diet[2,9], In contrast, on west-coast forests, like Rhum, it represents a smaller fraction of the diet (see Figure 4.6). In both areas, it is most heavily used in autumn and winter (see Figure 4.7).

Despite their abundance on many deer forests, purple moor grass, bog cotton and deer sedge are little used by deer, though purple moor grass and the draw shoots of bog cotton are sometimes eaten. In addition, bilberry (*Vaccinium myrtillus*) is often used in the eastern Highlands where it is abundant[5,6]. In coastal forests, sea-weed (mainly *Laminaria* species) is also eaten (Plate 4.2), especially between November and February, when it may account for as much as 10% of the total diet in some areas[16,17].

As would be expected from their diet, red deer in the Highlands usually show strong preferences for swards dominated by herbs,

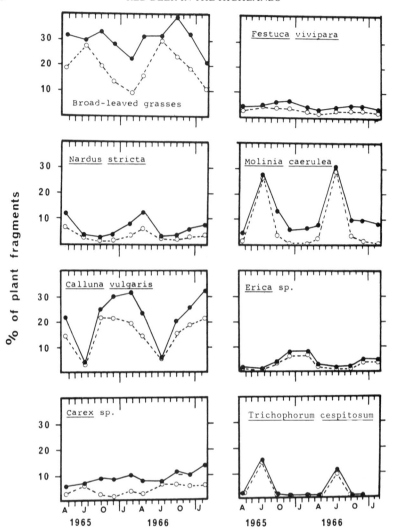

Figure 4.7 Percentages of different types of plant fragments in faeces collected between April 1965 and February 1967 in the western part of Rhum. The open circles show the percentage of fragments from living plants only, and the solid circles show those from living plus dead plants[38].

Agrostis, Festuca or *Deschampsia* though they will also forage for these grasses within swards dominated by *Molinia* and *Calluna*. In summer, stags and hinds in the North Block of Rhum used herb-rich *Agrostis/Festuca* grassland approximately ten times as heavily as heather moorland (Figure 4.8).

Within most plant communities and altitude levels, red deer

Plate 4.2 At low spring tide, hinds and followers feed on seaweed in the *Laminaria* beds in the North Block of Rhum. (Photograph: Fiona Guinness.)

usually select some areas or patches more than others. For example, in the North Block of Rhum they show an especially strong preference for feeding on patches of herb-rich grassland where the nitrogen content of the grass has been enhanced by the presence of herring-gull colonies[39] while, in other areas, they select patches of heather on the basis of their nitrogen content[5]. Taller stands of heather are preferred by deer to shorter stands[3,5,7] and their proximity to areas of preferred grassland may also be important. Within particular feeding bouts, red deer commonly eat a proportion of coarser forage in addition to the more nutritious grasses, and experiments under controlled conditions show that red deer will eat larger amounts of heather and can digest it more efficiently when it is fed in a mixture with grasses than when it is fed on its own[40]. Where possible, there are likely to be benefits in maintaining a finely-grained mosaic of vegetation communities.

In most areas of Scotland there is a marked seasonal pattern in the use of ground at different altitudes. In winter, lower ground is used heavily, partly because flushed grasslands, which provide red deer

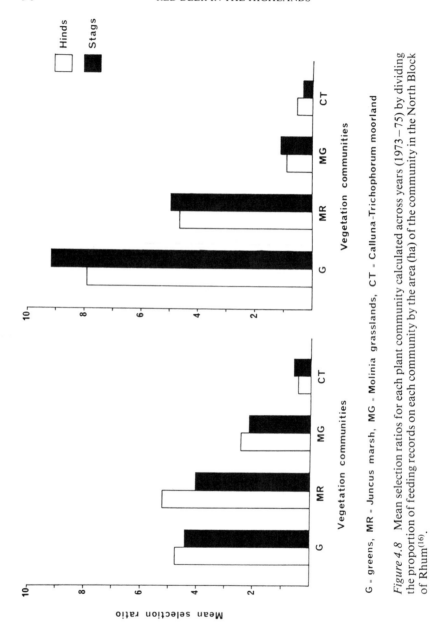

Figure 4.8   Mean selection ratios for each plant community calculated across years (1973 – 75) by dividing the proportion of feeding records on each community by the area (ha) of the community in the North Block of Rhum[16].

G = greens, MR = Juncus marsh, MG = Molinia grasslands, CT = Calluna-Trichophorum moorland

with an important part of their winter diet, are typically found at low altitude and partly because wind speed increases with altitude. Red deer rest and feed in sheltered sites whenever possible and the distribution of shelter has an important influence on the distribution of animals[41]. In exposed areas under extreme weather conditions, red deer may lose twice as much body heat as they do in shelter, thus

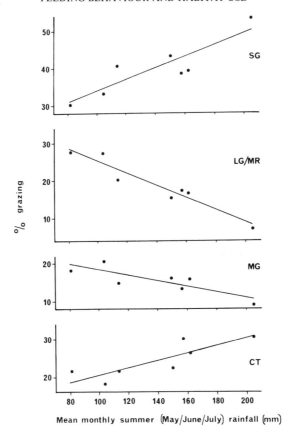

Figure 4.9 Proportion of grazing milk hinds seen on different plant communities between May and July in different years in the North Block of Rhum 1974–80, plotted on mean rainfall during these months in each year[46].
SG: short, herb-rich *Agrostis-Festuca* grasslands; LG/MR: longer, *Agrostis-Festuca* grassland or *Juncus* marsh; MG: *Molinia* dominated grassland; CT: *Calluna-Trichophorum* moorland.

increasing their energetic needs and increasing the danger of starvation[42]. Moreover, low temperatures and chilling conditions affect the rate of fermentation in the rumen, reducing the efficiency of their digestive system[43]. Tall vegetation, small plantations and small undulations in topography can all reduce wind speed substantially[42].

In late spring and summer, the deer use higher altitude levels to a greater extent, probably partly in response to the improved quality of vegetation there. Not only does the flush of spring growth occur later at higher altitudes but in heather, as well as some grasses, the concentration of sugars in the leaf increase with declining temperature and soil nitrogen levels[44,45]. However, harassment by biting and sucking flies, clegs (Tabanidae) and humans also plays a part.

Plate 4.3 Feeding specialists: a mature hind and her daughter graze in the graveyard of the ruined village at Kilmory, in the North Block of Rhum. For several years, only this hind and her progeny had learned to use this site. (Photograph: Fiona Guinness.)

While it is necessary to describe the feeding behaviour and habitat use of deer in terms of their average use of different foods or vegetation types, it is important to remember that these averages disguise pronounced differences between years. In wet summers, hinds on Rhum spend substantially more time on short, herb-rich grasslands and on heather-dominated swards and less on flushed grasslands (Figure 4.9). In addition, diet varies widely between individuals and family groups (Plate 4.3). For example, while heather provides just under 20% of the diet of the average deer in our study area some individuals spend more than 75% of their feeding time on heather-dominated swards. Similarly, while the average percentage of seaweed in the diet on Rhum is not much more than 5%, some individuals spend 15–20% of their feeding time eating seaweed while others rarely touch it.

4.4   DIFFERENCES IN DIET AND HABITAT USE BETWEEN STAGS AND HINDS

In many parts of the Highlands stags and hinds differ in their use of the habitat available. In general, stags feed more than hinds on swards that offer a higher availability of forage but lower food quality. They eat a lower proportion of narrow-leaved grasses and a higher proportion of heather, especially during the winter months[9,15]. Analysis of rumen nitrogen levels shows that they are lower in the food of stags and the size of the food particles in the rumen is larger, confirming that they eat a coarser, less digestible diet.

Differences in diet between stags and hinds are often associated with differences in the types of habitat occupied. Studies near Braemar, in the Eastern Highlands, and at Glenfeshie, in the Central Highlands, show that the winter ranges of hinds overlie base-rich rocks with more heavily mineralized soils which support larger areas of well-drained grassland than those of stags, which are commonly associated with base-poor rocks, less fertile soils and heather or *Molinia* dominated vegetation[4,9]. On west coast deer forests, like Rhum, hind ranges commonly include a higher proportion of well-drained grassland dominated by fescues, while stag ranges often have proportionately more flushed grassland, usually dominated by broad-leaved grasses including *Agrostis*[14,16]. However, even where stags and hinds use the same areas, stags usually continue to feed on coarser and less digestible vegetation than hinds, eating a lower proportion of herbs and narrow-leaved grasses[17].

In some areas, differences in diet between the sexes are linked with differences in their use of high and low ground. At Glen Dye, stags use higher ground than hinds in summer but lower in winter[1,2]. However, in other areas, stags use higher ground than hinds throughout the year[12] while, in our study area on Rhum, stags are more commonly seen at lower levels than hinds, especially in the summer months[16]. Local differences in vegetation, topography and disturbance are probably involved.

The most likely explanation of differences in diet between the sexes is that stags are more willing than hinds to exchange an increase in food abundance for a reduction in food quality on account of their larger body size. The rate of food intake probably does not increase proportionately with body size and, because of their larger body size and absolutely greater nutritional requirements, stags may be forced to feed in areas where food availability (and hence, intake rate) is relatively high[17]. This explanation is supported by evidence that increased use of swards strongly preferred by hinds reduces the standing crop of vegetation on them and gradually excludes stags from these areas. For example, an increase in hind numbers in the North Block of Rhum led to a decline in the extent to which stags used areas of short, well-drained grassland which were initially preferred by both sexes[17].

Differences in feeding behaviour also exist between milk and yeld hinds. During the summer months, milk hinds in the North Block of Rhum range less widely than yelds, spending more time feeding on herb-rich and *Agrostis/Festuca* grasslands and less time at relatively high altitudes[46]. These differences probably reflect their increased requirements for protein to cover the costs of lactation.

4.5 THE IMPACT OF DEER POPULATIONS ON THEIR HABITAT

On preferred swards, red deer quickly remove annual production, in some cases grazing the sward to an average height of less than a centimetre and preventing flowering. For example, even in the culled areas of Rhum where population density is lower than in the North Block, the deer remove over 90% of the total production on the short, herb-rich grasslands before September[14,18].

Grazing is an important component of the management of upland communities, and can help to maintain a wide array of plant species, to check the spread of a few dominant plants and to stimulate the production of palatable growth by dwarf shrubs. Studies of the effects of grazing on upland vegetation are numerous[5,26,47-60] but few of them relate specifically to red deer. Studies in north-east Scotland indicate that the effects of grazing in comparable densities by red deer are similar to those of grazing by sheep[5,51]. On Rhum, the reduction of grazing pressure following the removal of the island's sheep population was associated with a spread of *Molinia* and a reduction in species diversity, especially in areas of *Agrostis/Festuca* grassland[52]. The total elimination of grazing in experimental plots of grassland had an even greater effect, leading to an increase in *Poa* and *Festuca* and reducing the number of species per plot by over 40%[52]. Moderate grazing pressures also favour the lateral growth of heather, in some cases helping it to reassert its dominance more quickly[53,54].

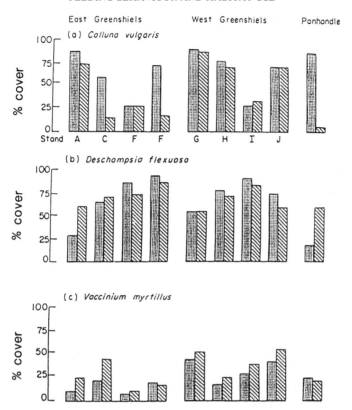

Figure 4.10 Changes in the percentage cover of three plant species in permanent quadrats between 1976 ▦ and 1979 ▧ following grazing by captive red deer at densities of between 110 and 250 per km²[51].

Very heavy grazing pressure by deer and domestic stock can depress the production of heavily used grasses in spring and can cause a reduction in heather and other dwarf shrubs[55,56]. For example, on hill ground stocked with 110−250 hinds per square kilometre over four years at the Glensaugh deer farm, heather cover showed a consistent decline[51]. In one area that carried over 700 hinds per square kilometre in some months (the Pan handle) heather was almost eradicated (see Figure 4.10). However, it is important to remember that these deer densities are over five times the maximum density commonly found on the open hill and that sheep, which have broadly similar effects on upland vegetation[6,56], are frequently maintained at densities of between 40 to 60 per square kilometre. In most areas of the Highlands, we suspect that the effects of sheep on the environment are more important than those of deer.

Even moderate deer densities can retard or prevent the regeneration of trees[58,59]. Research at Glenfeshie shows that birch, being deciduous, is eaten largely in summer while pine shows less seasonal variation. As might be expected, damage to saplings increases with the density of deer: at 25 deer per square kilometre, few saplings of birch, larch or pine live beyond ten years and all are dwarfed, while at 4 deer per square kilometre some saplings develop into trees[60]. At winter densities of below 2 deer per square kilometre, relatively little damage to saplings occurs. However, damage to growing seedlings is variable and is affected by a variety of other factors, including the distribution of deer and the availability of other sources of browse. The comparative effects of sheep and deer on tree regeneration are still unknown.

4.6 MUIRBURN AND DEER

On many Highland deer forests a proportion of the ground available is burnt each year to remove unpalatable, dead vegetation and to stimulate nutritious young growth for grouse, sheep or deer[50,62,63] (see Figure 4.11). It can also have an important effect on the use of less palatable swards by deer. For example, experimental burning of two areas of purple moor grass on Rhum led to a six- to eighteen-fold increase in the extent to which it was grazed by deer through the spring and early summer following the fire, though this decreased during the course of the summer as the grass matured[64]. By the following spring, grazing intensity on the burned areas was comparatively low though it was still around twice that on unburned areas. However, the longer term effects of poorly managed burning can include increased erosion and an increase in the abundance of unpalatable grasses and sedges (including *Molinia, Eriophorum* and *Trichophorum*) at the expense of heather and other dwarf shrubs that form an important component of the deers' winter diet[25,47,65].

The available studies emphasize the importance of burning relatively small strips and of maintaining a rotation of burning to ensure that the same patches are not burned too frequently[50,63]. On heather moors, patches may be burnt as soon as they reach 20–30 cm in height, approximately every 10–12 years on average moors. In contrast, purple-moor grass presents a dilemma. Although frequent burning (in some areas, every 3–4 years) helps to reduce the accumulation of dead matter and allow access by sheep or deer

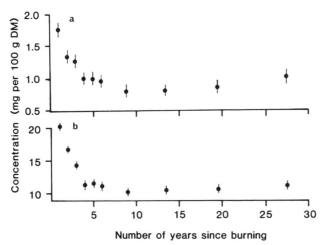

Figure 4.11   Mean nutrient content of leaf tips of current year's shoots of heather, *Calluna vulgaris*, in relation to time since burning (a) phosphorus (b) nitrogen. Vertical lines are 95% confidence limits[31].

to fresh growth in spring[63], burning frequencies as high as this are likely to damage other species, including heather, sometimes leading to their complete exclusion. Practical guides to burning practice are provided by the Red Deer Commission's booklets *Guide to Good Muirburn Practice*[66] and *Red Deer Management*[61].

The effects of burning on the reproductive performance and growth of red deer have yet to be investigated systematically. However, there is a suggestion that it can be appreciable. After the Nature Conservancy acquired Rhum in 1957, the 1750 sheep that had previously grazed the island were removed and the traditonal cull of about 40 stags and 40 hinds per year was raised to 100 stags and 140 hinds. Despite this, the body weight of hinds declined[67] and the proportion of animals breeding as two year olds fell from around 64% to 31%. However, in part of the island, fire breaks were burned to protect plantations and fecundity in these areas remained at its former level. A pronounced effect of burning on survival was also noted by Evans in the latter part of the last century on Jura[68].

4.7   SUPPLEMENTARY FEEDING

In some deer areas of the Highlands supplementary food (normally maize, hay, silage, potatoes, turnips, commercial deer cobs or

Plate 4.4 Shortly after casting their antlers in April, two mature stags on Rhum box at a feeding site. (Photograph: Fiona Guinness.)

mineral blocks) is provided for deer during the winter months. Usually, it is stags that take food but, in some areas, hinds, too, come to feed. Individual animals can obtain a substantial proportion of their food requirements from supplementary food. For example, some 'feeder' stags at Glenfeshie obtained around 17% of their daily maintenance requirements from feed and, when fed freely, would eat at least 50% of their total requirements[69].

On some forests, the aim of feeding is to reduce marauding or to decrease the emigration of stags to neighbouring estates. The provision of food obviously leads to a temporary movement of deer to the area of the feeding site[70] but its effects, if any, on population density and immigration and emigration by young or mature stags are not known. Regular feeding in the North Block of Rhum between 1968 and 1972 led to increased immigration of stags into the area and to an increase in the number of stags relative to hinds, which declined after feeding was terminated in 1972[16].

The effects of supplementary feeding on growth, reproduction and survival have not been studied systematically. Where deer are fed regularly throughout the winter, it would be surprising if this did not have some effect on their growth and condition. However, it is commonly the case that only a small proportion of animals in the area come to feed and that much of the food available is monopolised by a small number of dominant animals[69] (see Plate 4.4). As a result, feeding may have little effect on the average performance or antler growth of stags or on the average breeding success of hinds[71].

4.8   DEER, SHEEP AND CATTLE

Since red deer and sheep are the two most commercially important herbivores throughout most of the Highlands, considerable interest has focussed on their comparative nutritional requirements, digestion and habitat use. The digestive systems of red deer and sheep are very similar[22]. Both species digest cellulose by the action of similar microbial populations in their rumens and ruminal pH and concentrations of volatile fatty acids and ammonia vary little[72]. However, under captive conditions, red deer require 30–40% more energy per unit body weight for maintenance[22,40,73]. On the open hill, this difference is probably greater, for their coats provide less effective insulation and they lose heat more rapidly[74]. In addition, deer have a faster passage rate of food through the gut and digest grass diets less completely than sheep, though this difference does not apply to heather[22,40,62,75].

These differences do not indicate that sheep exploit moorland habitats more efficiently than deer. In captivity, deer eat coarser grasses and heather more readily than sheep[40,75] and comparisons of habitat use in the two species[10,12] show that although both show strong preference for *Agrostis/Festuca* grasslands and herb-rich swards, deer use higher altitude levels more than hill sheep throughout the year, feeding more on swards dominated by *Calluna, Molinia* and *Trichophorum* (Figure 4.12) and eating larger amounts of sedges and heather and proportionately less grass (Figure 4.13). It seems likely that in many areas of the Highlands and Islands mixed

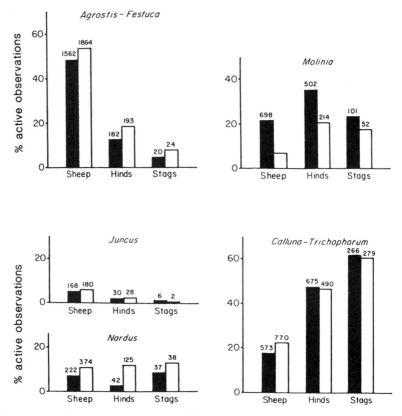

Figure 4.12 The percentage use of different plant communities by sheep, hinds and stags in summer (□) and winter (■) at Ardtornish, Argyll[12]. Values are for active, undisturbed animals only. Sample sizes are given above the columns.

stocking regimes of sheep and deer may offer higher productivity than would either species on its own[10].

How does the presence of sheep affect deer populations? Though no systematic attempt has yet been made to investigate the effects of sheep on habitat use by deer, it would be surprising if these were not considerable for, in many areas of Scotland, sheep numbers are substantially higher than deer numbers (Chapter 1). Comparisons between the relative use of different plant communities on Rhum (where no sheep are present) and at one site in Argyll (where similar ground carried 22 sheep per square kilometre) show that hinds and stags in Argyll spent considerably less time feeding on communities dominated by herbs, bents or fescues than on Rhum. In addition, negative correlations between geographical and temporal variation in sheep numbers and the density of deer (see Chapter 2) suggest that

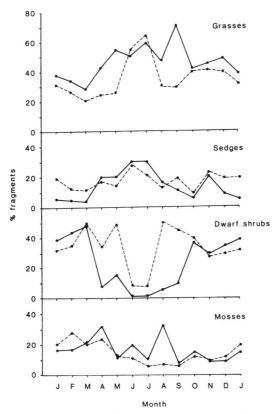

Figure 4.13 Proportional representation of fragments in faeces of deer (broken line) and sheep (solid line) at Killin, Perthshire throughout the year[10].

sheep numbers depress red deer density, though it is difficult to separate the effects of direct competition by deer and sheep from the indirect effects of sheep management and disturbance of deer. Sheep density could also influence the abundance of parasites shared by the two species (including liver fluke, lung worm, tapeworms and ticks) and may affect the incidence of common diseases (including leptospirosis, Avian TB and pneumonia[76,77]). However, the extent of their interactions and their impact on reproduction, growth and survival is still unknown.

Throughout some of their range, red deer also share their habitat with hill cattle. The beneficial effects of cattle on hill grazings have been recognised for many years[78,79], though they have rarely been clearly documented[48]. On Rhum, the introduction of Highland cattle led to the opening up of swards dominated by *Nardus* and *Molinia* for subsequent use by deer (Plate 4.5)[18]. Exclosure of

Plate 4.5 Highland cattle grazing in Glen Harris on Rhum. The introduction of Highland cattle on Rhum led to the opening up of swards dominated by *Nardus* and *Molinia* and to their increased use by deer. (Photograph: T. H. Clutton-Brock.)

cattle from parts of the island reduced the abundance of new growth and the subsequent use of these areas by deer[80]. However, the direct effects of cattle on the performance or density of deer has not yet been measured, though some evidence suggests that it could be appreciable. Introduction of cattle to two areas of upland grazing in southern Scotland was associated with an increase in sheep production of 18 and 37% respectively while total livestock production increased by 73 and 182%[81].

4.9 IMPLICATIONS FOR MANAGEMENT

Studies of the feeding ecology of Highland red deer have four main implications for their management. First, they emphasize that red deer are selective feeders, obtaining a large proportion of their diet from a small fraction of the ground available to them. The apparent abundance of food is illusory for a large proportion of upland vegetation cannot be used by the deer. Consequently, the removal of preferred habitat from their range for forestry or cultivation may have disproportionate effects on population density or reproductive performance. However, so far, there has been no systematic attempt to investigate the effects of afforestation on Highland deer populations and their magnitude is unknown.

Conversely, the improvement or extension of preferred habitat may lead to substantial increases in population density and to improvement in growth or reproduction. Several different approaches to improving habitat for deer are open to Highland managers. They include the provision of increased access to low ground, especially in winter and spring; the reduction of sheep stocks, especially in autumn and winter; burning purple moor grass or heather to improve their nutritive value; draining, liming or fertilising swards, especially if this increases the availability of bents and fescues at the expense of purple moor grass, deer sedge and bog cotton; the use of hill cattle to open up stands of purple moor grass and *Schoenus* fen and to create conditions where bents and fescues are likely to spread; and the planting of forestry belts to provide shelter in bad weather. In general, we believe these measures are more likely to affect population density and reproductive performance than the provision of winter food, which is usually monopolized by mature stags.

Second, the differences in habitat use between stags and hinds suggest that the requirements of the two sexes differ and management practices which aim to maximize the growth rates of stags and to minimize mortality and emigration may need to take this into account. The quality and availability of food in April and May, the last two months of gestation, apparently has a strong effect on the prenatal growth of calves and on their subsequent development (see Chapter 6) and any improvement in the quality or abundance of food in early spring may improve calf growth and reduce calf mortality throughout the first year of life. So, too, may improvements in feeding during June and July, when the food requirements of hinds are at their highest due to the heavy costs of lactation. For stags, the availability of food and shelter in early winter may have an important influence on their survival in late winter and early spring for most individuals enter the winter in poor condition after losing weight in the rut (see Figure 3.3). In addition, they appear to prefer taller vegetation than hinds do, perhaps because their larger body size requires a higher rate of food intake, and there is some evidence that hinds can exclude stags from the best grazings in winter by reducing the height of grass to levels at which stags cannot economically feed on it[17]. One of the most effective ways of increasing the number and size of resident stags may consequently be to reduce the numbers of wintering hinds and sheep.

Third, we suspect that further research will show that mixed stocking regimes offer higher productivity from hill ground than stocking with single species. As we describe in Section 4.8, there is some evidence that the presence of hill cattle improves the quality and quantity of vegetation available to deer and sheep. And though sheep commonly compete with deer, differences in habitat use between them indicate that a mixture of the two species probably makes fuller use of available plant production than would either species on its own. However, there is little solid information on the effects of sheep, deer and cattle on each other or of the consequences of different stocking combinations on upland vegetation. These effects may well vary with the relative density of the different species and may not be easy to predict in advance. This is an area where further research is badly needed.

Finally, it is clear that both commercial forestry plantations and natural woodlands attract deer, who can do substantial damage by browsing or barking trees (see Chapter 7). In many areas of natural pinewoods, pine seedlings are browsed so heavily by sheep and deer that regrowth is effectively prevented. Apart from the reduction of sheep and deer numbers to very low levels, there is no obvious solution to this problem at the moment[82].

4.10 SUMMARY

4.1   Almost all areas of red deer habitat in the Highlands share three important characteristics: a high proportion of grazing time is spent in a small proportion of the total range; plant production is strongly seasonal; and both diet and habitat use vary between years in response to changes in weather and population density.

4.2–4.4 Red deer graze for 10 to 12 hours per day. Though their appetite varies seasonally, grazing peaks occur before dawn and in the early evening. In most areas of the Highlands and Islands, broad leaved grasses (especially bents) and narrow leaved grasses (especially fescues) and heather provide most of the deers' diet. A higher proportion of grass is eaten in summer and of heather in winter. On many deer forests, stags feed more than hinds on swards that offer a higher availability of forage but lower food quality, especially during the winter months. These differences are probably a consequence of their larger body size.

4.5–4.6 Moderate levels of grazing by deer, as by sheep, help to maintain the number of species present and to stimulate the production of palatable growth by heather and other dwarf shrubs. However, excessive grazing pressure can reduce heather and cause local erosion. In addition, even moderate deer densities are sufficient to prevent the regeneration of natural woodland. Burning can have a substantial effect on the use of less palatable swards by deer and may temporarily increase carrying capacity and performance. However, excessive burning will remove heather, reducing the food available in winter.

4.7   On some deer forests, stag groups are fed in winter. The effects of supplementary feeding have not been studied systematically. In most cases, only a small proportion of resident animals, mainly stags, come to feed, and the demographic effects are probably small.

4.8   The effects on deer of competition with sheep have yet to be studied systematically. The available information suggests that the presence of sheep is associated with reduced use by deer of the bent/fescue swards preferred by both species. In contrast, grazing by cattle encourages subsequent use of longer swards by deer.

4.9   Research on the feeding ecology of red deer has at least four important implications for management. It suggests that because Highland deer obtain a large percentage of their diet from a small proportion of the ground available to them, both the exclosure and the improvement of preferred areas may have disproportionate effects on their population density, reproduction or survival; that one of the most effective ways of improving stag populations may be to control the numbers of hinds and sheep wintering in the same area; that mixed stocking regimes may make the most effective use of Highland habitats; and last, that even moderate densities of sheep and deer are sufficient to prevent the regeneration of many natural woodlands.

REFERENCES

1. Staines, B. W. (1970). *The Management and Dispersion of a Red Deer Population in Glen Dye, Kincardineshire.* Ph.D. thesis, University of Aberdeen.
2. Staines, B. W. (l.)1977. 'Factors affecting the seasonal distribution of red deer (*Cervus elaphus* L.) in Glen Dye, N.E. Scotland'. *Ann. Appl. Biol.*, **87**, 498–512.
3. Hewson, R. (1976). 'Grazing by mountain hare *Lepus timidus* L., red deer *Cervus elaphus* L. and red grouse *Lagopus* L. *scoticus* on heather moorland in north-east Scotland'. *J. Appl. Ecol.*, **13**, 657–666.
4. Watson, A. & Staines, B. W. (1978). 'Differences in the quality of wintering areas used by male and female red deer (*Cervus elaphus*) in Aberdeenshire'. *J. Zool.*, **186**, 544–550.
5. Moss, R., Welch, D. & Rothery, P. (1981). 'Effects of grazing by mountain hares and red deer on the production and chemical composition of heather'. *J. Appl. Ecol.*, **18**, 487–496.
6. Welch, D. (1984). 'Studies on the grazing of heather moorland in north-east Scotland. 1. Site descriptions and patterns of utilization'. *J. Appl. Ecol.*, **21**, 179–195.
7. Savory, L. J. (1986). 'Utilisation of different ages of heather on three Scottish moors by red grouse, mountain hares, sheep and deer'. *Holarctic Ecology*, **9**, 65–71.
8. Mitchell, B., Staines, B. W. & Welch, D. (1977). *Ecology of Red Deer: a Research Review Relevant to their Management in Scotland.* Inst. of Terrestrial Ecology, Cambridge.

9. Staines, B. W., Crisp, J. M. & Parish, T. (1982). 'Differences in food quality in red deer (*Cervus elaphus* L.) stags and hinds in winter'. *J. Appl. Ecol.*, **19**, 65–77.

10. Colquhoun, I. R. (1971). *The Grazing Ecology of Red Deer and Blackface Sheep in Perthshire, Scotland*. Ph.D. thesis, University of Edinburgh.

11. Jackes, A. D. (1973). *The Use of Wintering Grounds by Red Deer in Ross-shire*, Scotland. M. Phil. thesis, University of Edinburgh.

12. Osborne, B. C. (1984). 'Habitat use by red deer (*Cervus elaphus* L.) and hill sheep in the West Highlands'. *J. Appl. Ecol.*, **21**, 497–506.

13. Lowe, V. P. W. (1966). 'Observations on the dispersal of red deer on Rhum'. In: *Play, Exploration and Territory in Mammals*, ed. P. A. Jewell and C. Loizos, pp.211-228. Academic Press, London.

14. Charles, W. N., McCowan, D. & East, K. (1977). 'Selection of upland swards by red deer (*Cervus elaphus* L.) on Rhum'. *J. Appl. Ecol.*, **14**, 55–64.

15. Staines, B. W. & Crisp, J. M. (1978). 'Observations on food quality in Scottish red deer (*Cervus elaphus*) as determined by chemical analysis of the rumen contents'. *J. Zool. Lond.*, **185**, 253–259.

16. Clutton-Brock, T. H., Guinness, F. E. & Albon, S. D. (1982). *Red Deer: Behavior and Ecology of Two Sexes*. University of Chicago Press, Chicago.

17. Clutton-Brock, T. H., Iason, G. R. & Guinness, F. E. (1987). 'Sexual segregation and density-related changes in habitat use in male and female red deer (*Cervus elaphus*)'. *J. Zool. Lond.*, **211**, 275–289.

18. Gordon, I. (1986). 'The feeding strategies of ungulates on a Scottish moorland'. Ph.D. thesis, University of Cambridge.

19. Blaxter, K. L., Kay, R. N. B., Sharman, G. A. M., Cunningham, J. M. M. & Hamilton, W. J. (1974). *Farming the Red Deer*. H.M.S.O., London.

20. Kay, R. N. B. (1978). 'Seasonal changes of appetite in deer and sheep'. A.R.C. Research Review **5**, 13–15.

21. Suttie, J. M., Goodall, E. D., Pennie, K. & Kay, R. N. B., (1983). 'Winter feed restriction and summer compensation in red deer stags (*Cervus elaphus*)'. *Brit. J. Nutr.*, **50**, 737–747.

22. Kay, R. N. B. & Staines, B. W. (1981). 'The nutrition of red deer (*Cervus elaphus*)'. *Nutr. Abstr. Rev.*, **51**, 601–622.

23. McVean, D. N. & Ratcliffe, D. A. (1962). *Plant Communities of the Scottish Highlands*. Nature Conservancy Monograph No. **1**. H.M.S.O. London.

24. Darling, F. F. & Boyd, J. M. (1964). *The Highlands and Islands*. Collins, London.

25. Gimingham, C. H. (1972). *Ecology of Heathlands*. Chapman & Hall, London.

26. Welch, D. (1984a). 'Studies on the grazing of heather moorland in north-east Scotland. II. Response of heather'. *J. Appl. Ecol.*, **21**, 197–207.
27. Welch, D. (1984b). 'Studies of the grazing of heather moorland in north-east Scotland. III. Floristics'. *J. Appl.Ecol.*, **21**, 209–225.
28. Gloyne, R. W. (1968). 'Some climatic influences affecting hill-land productivity'. *Occ. Symp. Brit. Grassl. Assoc.*, No. **4**, 9–15.
29. Albon, S. D. (1983). 'Ecological aspects of growth, reproduction and mortality in female red deer'. Ph.D. thesis, University of East Anglia.
30. Albon, S. D. & Clutton-Brock, T. H. (1988). 'Temporal variation in climate and the population dynamics of red deer in Scotland'. In: *Ecological Change in the Uplands*, ed. M. B. Usher & D. Thompson, pp. 93–107, Blackwells, Oxford.
31. Miller, G. R. (1979). 'Quantity and quality of the annual production of shrubs and flowers by *Calluna vulgaris* in North-east Scotland'. *J. Ecol.*, **67**, 109–129.
32. Harper, J. A., Harn, J. H., Bentley, W.W. & Yocom, C. F. (1967). 'The status and ecology of the Roosevelt elk in California'. *Wildl. Monogr.*, **16**, 49.
33. Boyd, R. J. (1970). 'Elk of the White River Plateau, Colorado'. *Tech. Publs. Colo. Game, Fish and Parks Div.* No.**25**.
34. Dzieciolowski, R. (1969). *The Quantity, Quality and Seasonal Variation of Food Resources Available to Red Deer in Various Environmental Conditions of Forest Management*. Polish Academy of Sciences, Forest Research Institute, Warsaw.
35. Eygenraam, J. A. (1959). 'On the management of red deer in the Netherlands'. **ITBON** Wertz, **42**.
36. Jensen, P. V. (1968). 'Food selection of the Danish red deer (*Cervus elaphus* L.) as determined by examination of the rumen contents'. *Danish Rev. Game Biol.*, **51**, 1–44.
37. Gibb, J. A. & Flux, J. E. C. (1973). 'Mammals'. In: *The Natural History of New Zealand*, ed. G. R. Williams, pp. 334–371. Reed, Wellington.
38. Charles, W. N., McCowan, D. & East, K. Unpublished data, analysed in Reference [16].
39. Iason, G. R., Duck, C. D. & Clutton-Brock, T. H. (1986). 'Grazing and reproductive success of red deer: the effect of local enrichment by gull colonies'. *J. Anim. Ecol.*, **55**, 507–515.
40. Milne, J. A., MacRae, J. L., Spence, A. M. & Wilson, S. (1978). 'A comparison of the voluntary intake and digestion of a range of forages at different times of year by the sheep and red deer (*Cervus elaphus*)'. *Brit. J. Nutr.*, **40**, 347–357.
41. Staines, B. W. (1976). 'The use of natural shelter by red deer in north-east Scotland'. *J. Zool.*, **180**, 1–8.

42. Grace, J. & Easterbee, N. (1979). 'The natural shelter for red deer (*Cervus elaphus*) in a Scottish glen'. *J. Appl. Ecol.*, **16**, 37–48.

43. Hobson, P. N., Mann, S. O., Summers, R. & Staines, B. W. (1976). 'Rumen function in red deer, hill sheep and reindeer in the Scottish Highlands'. *Proc. R. Soc. Edinb.*, B. **75**, 181–198.

44. Grace, J. & Woolhouse, H. W. (1970). 'A physiological and mathematical study of growth and productivity of a *Calluna-Sphagnum* community'. *J. Appl. Ecol.*, **7**, 363–381.

45. Mathews, M. O. (1972). 'Red deer, heather, sugar percent, altitude'. B.Sc. thesis, Department of Forestry and Natural Resources, Edinburgh.

46. Clutton-Brock, T. H., Iason, G. R., Albon, S. D. & Guinness, F. E. (1982). 'Effects of lactation on feeding behaviour and habitat use in wild red deer hinds'. *J. Zool.*, **198**, 227–236.

47. McVean, D. N. & Lockie, J. D. (1969). *Ecology and Land Use in Upland Scotland*. Edinburgh University Press, Edinburgh.

48. Hodgson, J. (1985). 'Grazing and its influence on hill vegetation'. In: *Vegetation Management in Northern Britain*, ed. R. B. Murray, 21–31. British Crop Protection Council, Croydon, U.K.

49. Ball, D. F., Dale, J., Sheall, J. & Heal, O. W. (1982). *Vegetation Change in Upland Landscapes*. Institute of Terrestrial Ecology, Cambridge.

50. Hobbs, R. J. & Gimingham, C. H. (1987). 'Vegetation, fire and herbivore interactions in heathland'. *Advances in Ecological Research,* **16**, 87–173.

51. Grant, S. A., Hamilton, W. J. & Souter, W. (1981). 'The responses of heather-dominated vegetation in North-east Scotland to grazing by red deer'. *J. Ecol.*, **69**, 189–204.

52. Ball, M. E. (1974). 'Floristic changes on grasslands and heaths on the Isle of Rhum after a reduction or exclusion of grazing'. *J. Environ. Mgmt.*, **2**, 299–318.

53. Gimingham, C. H. (1949). 'The effects of grazing on the balance between *Erica cinnerea* L. and *Calluna vulgaris* L. in upland heath, and their morphology responses'. *J. Ecol.*, **37**, 100–119.

54. Grant, S. (1968). 'Heather regeneration following burning: a survey'. *J. Br. Grassland Soc.*, **23**, 26–33.

55. Welch, D. (1974). 'The floristic composition of British upland vegetation in relation to grazing'. *Land*, **1**, 59–68.

56. Miles, J., Welch, D. & Chapman, S. B. (1978). 'Vegetation and management in the uplands'. In: *Upland Land Use in England and Wales*, ed. W. O. Heal, 77–95. Countryside Commission, Leeds.

57. Grant, S. & Hunter, R. F. (1968). 'Interactions of grazing and burning on heather moors and their implications for heather management'. *J. Br. Grassland Soc.*, **23**, 285–293.

58. Miller, G. R. & Cummins, R. P. (1974). 'Liability of saplings to grazing on red deer range'. In: *Institute of Terrestrial Ecology Report 1971–1973*, pp. 31–33, N.E.R.C., London.

59. Kinnaird, J. W. (1974). 'Effect of site conditions on the regeneration of birch (*Betula pendula* Roth and *B. pubescens* Ehrh)'. *J. Ecol.*, **62**, 467–472.

60. Holloway, C. W. (1967). *The Effect of Red Deer and Other Animals on Naturally Regenerated Scots Pine*. Ph.D. thesis, University of Aberdeen.

61. Red Deer Commission (1981). *Red Deer Management*. H.M.S.O., Edinburgh.

62. Miller, G. R. & Watson, A. (1974). 'Some effects of fire on vertebrate herbivores in the Scottish Highlands'. *Proc. Annual Tall Timbers Fire Ecol. Conf.*, **13**, 39–64.

63. Gimingham, C. H. (1985). 'Muirburn'. In: *Vegetation Management in Northern Britain*, ed. R. B. Murray, 71–75. British Crop Protection Council, Croydon, U.K.

64. Miles, J. (1971). 'Burning *Molinia*-dominant vegetation for grazing by red deer'. *J. Br. Grassland Soc.*, **26**, 247–250.

65. Nicholson, I. A. (1974). 'Red deer range and problems of carrying capacity in the Scottish Highlands'. *Mammal Review*, **4**, 103–118.

66. Red Deer Commission (1980). *Guide to Good Muirburn Practice*. H.M.S.O., Edinburgh.

67. Lowe, V. P. W. (1971). 'Some effects of a change in estate management on a deer population'. In: *The Scientific Management of Plant and Animal Communities*, ed. E. Duffey & A. S. Watt, 437–456. Blackwell Scientific Publications Ltd, Oxford.

68. Evans, H. (1890). *Some Account of Jura Red Deer*. Private publication, Carter, Derby.

69. Wiersema, G. J. (1974). 'Observations on the supplementary winter feeding of red deer on an estate in the central Highlands'. M.Sc. thesis, University of Wageningen, The Netherlands.

70. Dunnet, S. C. (1975). 'Diversionary feeding and red deer'. *Deer*, **3**, 447–452.

71. Mutch, W. E. S., Lockie, J. D. & Cooper, A. N. (1976). *The red deer in South Ross: a Report on Wildlife Management in the Scottish Highlands*. Department of Forestry & Natural Resources, University of Edinburgh.

72. Maloiy, G. M. O. & Kay, R. N. B. (1971). 'A comparison of digestion in red deer and sheep under controlled conditions'. *Quart. J. Exp. Physiol.*, **56**, 257–266.

73. Milne, J. A., MacRae, J. C., Spence, A. M. & Wilson, S. (1976). 'Intake and digestion of hill-land vegetation by red deer and sheep'. *Nature*, **263**, 763–764.

74. Brockway, J. M. & Maloiy, G. M. O. (1968). 'Energy metabolism of red deer'. *J. Physiol. Lond.*, **194**, 22–24.

75. Kay, R. N. B. & Goodall, E. C. (1976). 'The intake, digestibility and retention time of roughage diets by red deer (*Cervus elaphus*) and sheep'. *Proc. Nutr. Soc.*, **35**, 98A.

76. Dunn, A. M. (1969). 'The wild ruminant as reservoir host of helminth infection'. In: *Diseases in Free-living Animals*, ed. A. McDiarmid, 221–248. Academic Press, London.

77. Alexander, T. L. (1986). *Management and Diseases of Deer.* Veterinary Deer Society, London.

78. Cameron, A. G. (1923). *The Wild Red Deer of Scotland.* Blackwood & Sons, Edinburgh and London.

79. Nicholson, I. A., Patterson, I. S. & Currie, A. (1970). 'A study of vegetational dynamics: selection by sheep and cattle in *Nardus* pasture'. In: *Animal Populations in Relation to their Food Resources*, ed. A. Watson, 129–143. Blackwell Scientific Publications Ltd, Oxford.

80. Gordon, I. (1988). 'Facilitation of red deer grazing by cattle and its impact on red deer performance'. *J. Appl. Ecol*, **25**, 1–10.

81. Peart, J. N. (1963). 'Increased production from hill pastures. Sourhope trials with cattle and sheep'. *Scottish Agriculture*, **42**, 147–151.

82. Bunce, R. G. H. & Jeffers, J. N. R. (1977). *Native Pinewoods of Scotland.* Institute of Terrestrial Ecology, Cambridge.

5 Population Density, Reproduction and Survival

5.1 INTRODUCTION

In many parts of Scotland, red deer numbers on the hill have been rising since the turn of the century (see Chapter 2). Though part of the increase has been caused by the occupation of new ground, population density has also risen on established deer ground. Unfortunately, the effects of increasing density have been monitored in few sites and we know little about them. It is sometimes suggested that high population density may be associated with unstable populations which peak and then crash in poor years[1]. But is this really the case? Or do rising numbers gradually stabilise as increasing population density and declining food availability reduce recruitment and survival[2]? High population density need not necessarily even be associated with a major reduction in growth, for the effects of competition may fall principally on the poorest animals in the population.

In this chapter, we describe the effects of increasing population density on fecundity (Section 5.2), mortality (Section 5.3), growth (Section 5.4) and dispersal (Section 5.5) and the relative importance of these changes in limiting population growth. In Section 5.6, we raise the question of what resources are likely to limit population size and when they are likely to act while the same section discusses the implications of density-dependent effects for management.

Investigating population regulation and the effects of population density in red deer is complicated by the fact that the sexes are usually segregated. Consequently, it is not safe to assume that it is the combined density of both sexes that affects the availability of resources. Because mature stags and hinds use different areas throughout much of the year (see Chapter 4) the growth, survival and reproductive performance of hinds and their followers is more likely to be affected by competition with other hinds and juveniles than by competition with stags[3,4]. The growth and survival of stags might also be affected mainly by their own density. However, evidence that stags are excluded from preferred habitat by rising hind numbers[3] suggests that stag performance may be more strongly affected by *hind* numbers than by stag density[5]. For example, in our study area on Rhum the growth and survival of stags are better predicted by the density of hinds than by stag density[5]. For this reason, most of our graphs show changes in reproduction and survival plotted against the number of hinds alone.

The effects of variation in population density have usually been

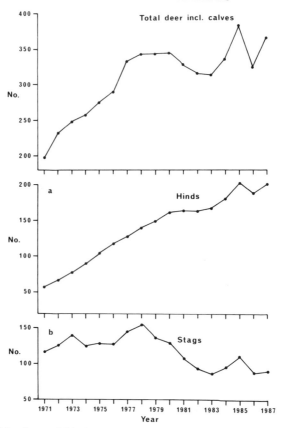

Figure 5.1   Numbers of hinds and stags resident in the North Block of Rhum following the cessation of culling in 1972.

investigated either by comparisons between areas of high and low density[6,7,8] or by examining the effects of changes in density within the same area[4,5,7,9]. Both approaches have their problems. Geographical comparisons are commonly confounded by differences in the quality of ground which can generate major differences in deer density that do not affect recruitment or survival (see Chapter 2) while correlated changes in climate or other environmental factors may confound the effects of temporal changes in population density. This emphasizes the need for control areas, where population density is maintained at an approximately constant level, as it is outside the North Block of Rhum. In addition, it underlines the importance of understanding the effects of density-independent variables, including variation in climate (see Chapter 6).

The effects of changing population density have only been

investigated within three populations of deer living on the open hill
– at Glen Dye[7], at Glenfeshie[6,9,10] and on Rhum[4,5,11]. At Glen
Dye, an initial population of around 10 deer per square kilometre
was reduced to around 3.4 deer per square kilometre by heavy
culling over seven years[7]. At Glenfeshie, deer density varied
between 10 and 16 per square kilometres between 1967 and 1974 and
fecundity, recruitment and survival were monitored each year[9,10].
Lastly, the most detailed study of the effects of changing stocking
rate has been carried out on Rhum (see Chapter 1). In 1971, the 12
square kilometre North Block of the island supported a population
of 57 hinds and 116 stags, a total density (including calves) of 18.4
deer per square kilometre. Culling in the North Block ceased in
1971/1972 and by 1983 the population had increased to 166 hinds
and 86 stags, a total density of 25 animals per square kilometre (see
Figure 5.1). Around 95% of the deer resident in the area could be
recognised as individuals (see Chapter 1), making it possible to
measure changes in immigration and emigration as well as in
reproduction and survival. Comparable information on calf/hind
ratios, growth and mortality was collected over the rest of the island
where a density of around 17 deer per square kilometre was
maintained by an average cull of 12%[5].

5.2   POPULATION DENSITY AND FECUNDITY

There is a close relationship between stocking rate and the fecundity
of hinds. The age of hinds at first breeding is especially sensitive to
changes in population density. Where food is abundant, many hinds
can breed for the first time at eighteen months[6]. For example,
following the reduction in population size, pregnancy rates among
samples of yearling hinds shot at Glen Dye were around 64% (see
Chapter 2) and, across Scottish deer populations, the proportion of
yearlings pregnant declines as density increases[6] (see Figure 7.2).
On many Highland deer forests, pregnant yearlings are seldom or
never observed and the majority of hinds conceive for the first time
as two-year-olds or as three-year-olds if density is particularly high.
As population density increased in the North Block of Rhum, the
proportion of hinds that conceived as two-year-olds fell from
around 65% when hind density was low to approximately 10% when
it was high[5].

Our research on Rhum also shows that rising population density

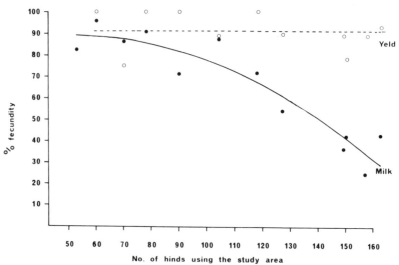

Figure 5.2   Changes in the percentage of milk and yeld hinds that produced calves in each year as hind density rose in the North Block of Rhum following the cessation of culling in 1972[13].

has a strong effect on the fecundity of milk hinds, but little or no effect on that of mature yeld hinds. As hind numbers increased in the North Block, the population of milk hinds calving fell from 90% at low population density to around 30% at high density (Figure 5.2) while the fecundity of three-year-olds fell from around 70% to around 10%[12]. Similar results were observed at Glenfeshie where fecundity of milk hinds fell from 80% to 30% as hind numbers increased from 900 to 1200[9]. In contrast, the change in fecundity of yeld hinds was only from 100% to 90% at Glenfeshie and on Rhum no systematic decline was detected[9].

As in other mammals, the fecundity of red deer hinds is closely related to their weight (Figure 5.3). In all five of the populations where the relationship between body weight and fecundity has been examined, there is a critical weight threshold below which hinds rarely conceive[8,14,15]. Changes in food availability probably affect fecundity in two different ways. First, they may reduce the body weight of hinds in autumn, though this has yet to be demonstrated. If so, a higher proportion of animals fall below this threshold and the percentage that become fertile may decline. Second, they may alter the weight at which animals are likely to conceive. As Figure 5.4a shows, the weight threshold is higher in some populations than in others: for example, in deer from Scarba, only 30% of animals

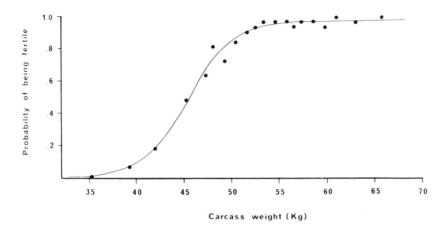

Figure 5.3   Probability of being fertile (proportion pregnant) among yeld hinds at Glenfeshie plotted against (larger) carcase weight[8]. For example, the curve shows that yeld hinds with a (larger) carcase weight of 42 kg had a 0.2 chance of being pregnant whereas those with a carcase weight of 52 kg had a 0.9 chance of being pregnant.

weighing 50 kg were pregnant while 90% of deer were pregnant at this weight at Glen Dye. Across the five populations shown in Figure 5.4a differences in the percentage of hinds that were pregnant (fertility) *at a given body weight* were themselves related to population density (see Figure 5.4b) and, in high density populations, animals had to be heavier in order to conceive[8]. For example, hinds from Scarba had to weigh 52.5 kg to have a 50% chance of conceiving while those from Glen Dye had a 50% chance of conceiving at the extremely low weight of 42 kg. Changes in population density between years on Rhum were also associated with similar shifts in the relationship between fertility and female body weight[8].

As well as affecting fecundity, population density has an important influence on the timing of conception and thus on the birth dates of calves. As population density increased in the North Block of Rhum, the average birth date of calves changed from June 2 to June 16 (see Figure 5.5), presumably because the average date of conception gradually changed from September 25 to October 9. This change was a major cause of increased calf mortality at high density since the over-winter survival of late-born calves was low[11].

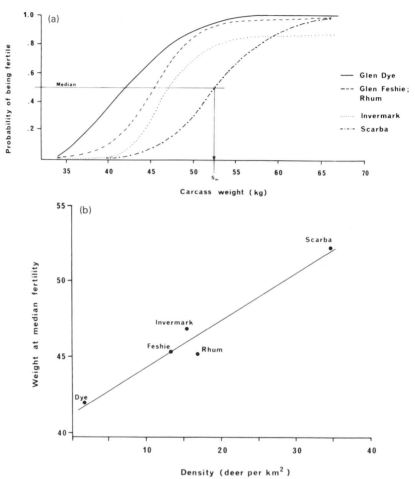

Figure 5.4 (a) Fertility of yeld hinds (proportion of animals pregnant) plotted against larder carcase weight for 5 different Highland populations[8]. (b) Weight at median fertility for yeld hinds plotted on total population density[8].

5.3 POPULATION DENSITY AND MORTALITY

It is important to distinguish clearly between the total numbers of animals dying and the mortality rate, for these are sometimes confused. When an area of ground supports a large number of animals absolutely, more individuals can be expected to die each year. This need not indicate that the percentage dying (the mortality rate) has increased.

In many animals, the effects of increasing population density fall primarily on the young. In Highland red deer, juvenile mortality

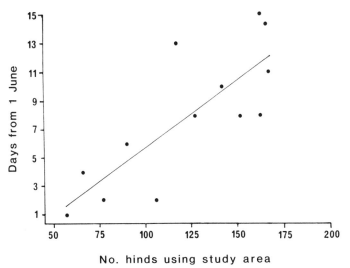

Figure 5.5   Median date of calving (days after June 1) in the North Block of Rhum, 1971–1983, plotted against the numbers of hinds using the 12 km² study area[11].

peaks during the first two weeks of life and again at the end of the first and second winters (see Chapter 3). It is important to distinguish clearly between neonatal mortality and calf mortality in winter for they have different causes. In the North Block of Rhum neonatal mortality of calves averaged approximately 20% and was not consistently related to changes in population density (Figure 5.6a), even when weather effects were allowed for[5]. In contrast, the mortality of calves during their first winter rose with increasing population density from less than 5% to nearly 40% (Figure 5.6b), while the mortality of yearlings rose from 0% to 30%. As a result of lower fecundity and increased calf mortality, the number of calves per hundred hinds in spring fell from 45–50 calves per hundred hinds to 30–35 per hundred (Figure 5.6c). Calf/hind ratios over the rest of the island (where the cull was continued and population density was approximately constant) showed no consistent change over the same period, remaining at around 38 calves per hundred hinds[5].

As in many other mammals[16], high population density and low food availability affects the survival of males more than that of females. As hind density increased in our study area on Rhum, the mortality of males during their first two years of life rose from less than 10% to around 60% while the mortality of females over the same period increased from around 10% to 30% (Figure 5.7).

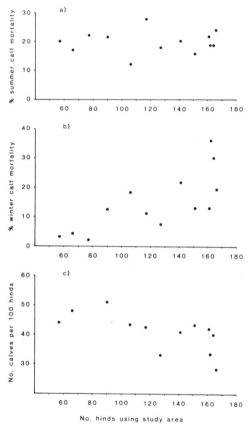

Figure 5.6   The proportion of calves in the North Block of Rhum in 1971–1983 (a) that died in their first summer (June-September); (b) that died in their first winter (October-April); and (c) the number of calves per 100 hinds in spring, plotted against the number of hinds using the 12 km² study area[5].

Across a wide variety of mammals and birds sex differences in mortality among juveniles exposed to food shortage increase in relation to the difference in body size between the sexes (see Figure 8.2).

The effects of population density on adult mortality appear to be weaker than on juvenile mortality. Where the effects of winter weather were controlled for (see Chapter 6), adult mortality in our study area tended to rise with density, though this effect was not large. Differences in adult mortality between the North Block and the rest of the island were most marked after wet autumns.

These results suggest that, in unculled populations, juvenile mortality may be more important in regulating deer numbers than

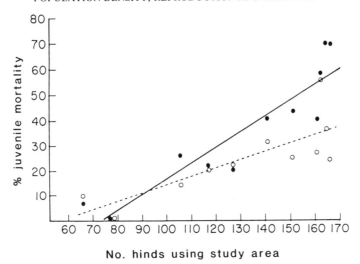

Figure 5.7 Mortality during the first two years of life among males (●) and females (o) born between 1971 and 1982 in the red deer population of the North Block of Rhum[16].

adult mortality. Theoretically, changes in population size could be a consequence of changes in fecundity, in juvenile mortality or in adult mortality. A statistical technique called key factor analysis makes it possible to compare the extent to which each of these components contributes to changes in numbers and the extent to which they increase or decline with density[17,18]. The method consists of expressing each component of each year's total mortality including reductions in fecundity, as the logarithm of the ratio of population size before and after the mortality in question has acted. The total mortality in each year (K) is the sum of all the separate sub-mortalities (k_1, k_2, k_3 and so on). When total mortality (K) and its sub-mortalities ($k_1 - k_n$) are plotted against time, it is usually possible to see which sub-mortality is responsible for changes in K. Used on information from the North Block of Rhum, this technique shows that although changes in fecundity between 1971 and 1983 were correlated with changes in total mortality (K), changes in over-winter mortality (k_4) exerted a stronger influence on K (see Figure 5.8). Sub-division of winter mortality showed that changes in the mortality of calves were substantially more important than changes in adult mortality and increased more rapidly as population density rose[5].

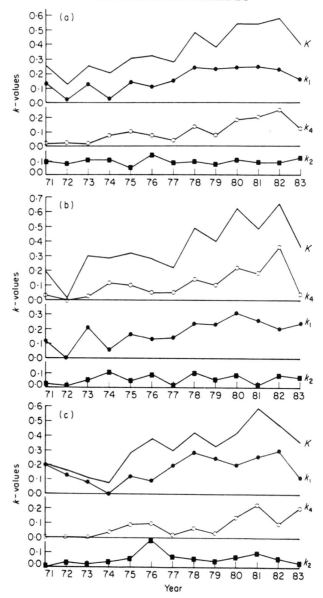

Figure 5.8   *K*-values, 1971–1983, for (a) stags and hinds combined (b) stags only and (c) hinds only. *K*, total mortality including reductions in fecundity; k_1, reduction in fecundity; k_2, summer mortality (mostly calves); k_3, net emigration (emigration – immigration); k_4, winter mortality[5].

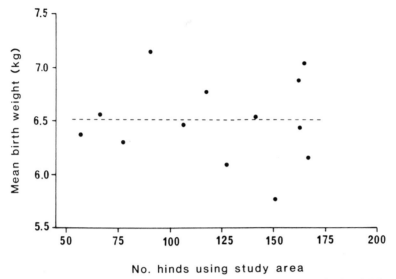

Figure 5.9 Mean birth weights of calves born in the North Block of Rhum, 1971–1983, plotted against the number of hinds using the 12 km² study area[11].

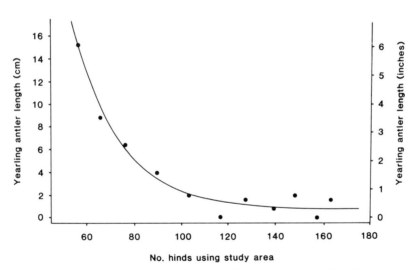

Figure 5.10 The median length of cleaned antlers of sixteen-month-old stags in the North Block of Rhum, 1972–1982, plotted against the number of hinds using the 12 km² study area. (Redrawn from [13]).

5.4 POPULATION DENSITY AND GROWTH

Changes in population density appear to have little effect on the birth weights of calves. As numbers rose in the North Block of Rhum, calf birth weights did not change consistently (Figure 5.9). However, whereas light-born calves had approximately the same chances of survival as heavy-born calves when population density was low, at high density, they were around four times less likely to survive[11]. In addition, the growth of yearlings was seriously affected by rising population density: the antler growth of yearling stags showed a rapid decline as soon as the numbers rate began to increase (see Figure 5.10). So, too, did the antler weight of adult stags, which declined by approximately 20% between 1971 and 1982 (see Figure 5.11).

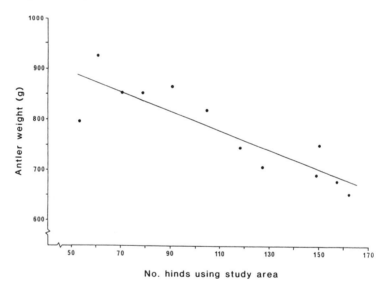

Figure 5.11 The median weight of single cast antlers of 7-year-old stags in the North Block of Rhum, 1971–1982, plotted against the number of hinds using the 12 km² study area[13].

5.5 POPULATION DENSITY AND DISPERSAL

Little is known of the effects of population density on either temporary or permanent dispersal though these may be of crucial importance in smaller deer forests where the number of stags that can be culled may depend on rates of immigration and emigration. Do high hind numbers attract immigrant stags during the rut? How does the density of hinds or adult stags affect permanent dispersal and immigration by young stags? And how does population density affect the dispersal of hinds? At the moment, we have no clear answers to these questions.

On Rhum, increasing hind density in the North Block was not associated with any pronounced increase in emigration by hinds though groups living on the periphery of the Block ranged more widely as density rose. Even at high density, emigration was rare: between 1974 and 1982 only nine hinds over one year old emigrated from the Block and eight immigrated into the population. The Block only represents around a fifth of the area of Rhum and no physical barriers prevented emigration and immigration.

Among stags, increasing hind density may discourage permanent immigration by young stags. As hind density rose on Rhum, stags used areas preferred by hinds progressively less (see Chapter 4) and fewer stags settled in areas of high hind density. The number of stags immigrating permanently into the Block declined though the number of migrant stags visiting the Block temporarily during the rut may have increased.

In many areas of the Scottish mainland, crop raiding and damage to forestry by deer living on the open hill present problems. As the population density of deer increases, the amount of damage can be expected to rise as a consequence of the increase in numbers. Whether high deer density also increases the tendency for individual deer to maraud, thus causing a disproportionate increase in damage at high population densities, is not yet known.

5.6 IMPLICATIONS FOR MANAGEMENT

Research on the effects of increasing population density shows that most aspects of reproduction, survival and growth decline as the density of hinds increases. Similar changes have been observed in elk[19,20] as well as in other ungulates[2]. The growth and survival of stags appears to be more strongly affected by rising population density than that of hinds, perhaps as a result of their greater nutritional requirements[4,16,19] and antler size, in particular, declines as population density rises.

These results emphasize the need to consider what density of deer it is best to maintain. Three points regarding this decision are clear:

First, the optimal density of deer will depend on the aims of management and these must be clearly defined before any management policy can be assessed. For example, the density which would have produced the maximum number of animals per year from our study area on Rhum was considerably higher than the density which maximised antler growth in stags, fecundity or calf survival. In general, where the aim of management is to maximize venison yield, a relatively high density of hinds is likely to be advantageous (though this may be impractical where damage to forestry or crop raiding is a problem). In contrast, where the aim is to maximize body or antler size, a low density in hinds is probably desirable.

Second, it is clear that there is no single ideal density for all Highland habitats. Geographical variation in topography, soil type and competition with domestic herbivores affect the amount of food available to the deer and hence the number that ground can sustain (see Chapter 2). Especially where deer have access to low ground, numbers can reach relatively high levels without growth and reproductive performance being severely depressed[22].

Third, the number of deer that ground can support is unlikely to be stable and can be expected to vary with changes in climate or other environmental factors. As we show in Chapters 2 and 6, long-term trends in weather as well as in other agricultural practices can have an important influence on reproduction as well as on deer numbers.

Assuming that the aim of management is to maximize the total number of animals that can be culled each year, what level of population density is likely to achieve this? Our research on Rhum provides an illustration of how the sustainable yield (the number of animals that can be culled without reducing population size) is likely to change with population density. After culling was ceased in 1972, the number of hinds that could have been removed from the study population each year without reducing its size initially rose, but after population size had reached 99, the sustainable yield fell as a result of lower reproductive rates at high density (Figure 5.12a). Had the population been culled at any level below the rate of recruitment, the increase in hind numbers would have been slower and the sustainable yield would have been slightly higher due to the lower proportion of old animals in the population, but the pattern of change would have been similar. In a fully self-contained population where immigration and emigration of stags cannot occur, the sustainable yield of stags is likely to change with increasing population density in much the same way as the sustainable yield of hinds

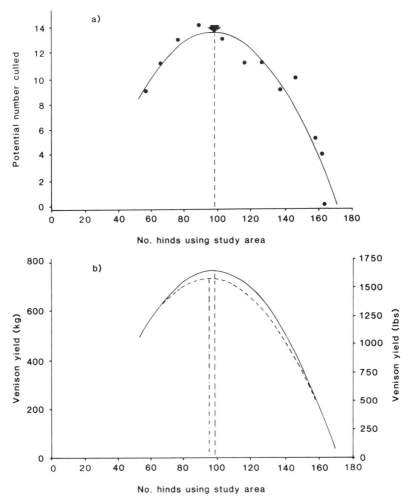

Figure 5.12 Changes in the potential yield of red deer hinds from the North Block of Rhum at different population densities, based on measures of recruitment after natural mortality: (a) number of hinds (b) venison yield, calculated assuming an average larder carcase weight of 60 kg (solid line) and a gradual reduction in carcase weight of 10% (interrupted curve).

though the density that will produce the maximum yield may be slightly lower for stags on account of the greater reduction in the survival of juvenile males as density increases (Figure 5.7).

If our aim had instead been to maximize the amount of *venison* produced by annual hind culls, we should have needed to take into account any effects of increasing density on carcase weight. These relationships are unknown but we can calculate how large their influence might have been, assuming different effects of density on carcase weight. For example, Figure 5.12b shows the venison yield that our study area on Rhum would have produced at different hind densities, assuming (a) no change in carcase weight with increasing density (top, continuous curve) and (b) a gradual reduction in body weight with increasing density, rising to 10% less than the observed weight in 1971/72 (lower, interrupted curve). As the figure shows, even a 10% reduction in weight with increasing density would only have reduced the optimal population size for venison production from 99 to 96. The inclusion of stags would probably increase this difference for their growth appears to be more strongly affected by food availability than that of hinds (see Chapter 7). However, where the aim is to maximize venison yield, it is likely to be advantageous to maintain a female bias in the populations, killing stags soon after the age of five years, when their rate of growth begins to decline (see Chapter 3).

Our estimates for the North Block of Rhum illustrate the problems of calculating the population density which will maximize cull size, even in an area where the effects of density on reproduction and survival have been studied in detail. The effects of population density on reproduction, survival and dispersal are likely to vary from area to area and cannot safely be extrapolated between populations. Where these relationships are known, sustainable yield can be calculated[23] but it is unlikely that these figures will ever be available for the majority of deer populations. In this situation, we believe that the best advice that can be given to managers is to decide their objectives clearly and then to proceed by trial and error, treating successive changes in culling rate as experiments[24]. Deer density can be changed upwards or downwards by reducing or increasing the annual cull. By gradually increasing cull size after the population has attained its new level, it is possible to determine the size of cull that the population can sustain while changes in carcase weight and antler size at different densities can be monitored from the annual cull. This approach obviously requires an annual or biennial estimate of deer numbers, though this need not be a total count so long as it includes a representative sample of animals from the population (see Chapter 8).

5.7 SUMMARY

5.1−5.3 Increasing population density has a pronounced effect on the fecundity of hinds. Median age at first breeding in Highland deer rises from one year where population density is low relative to the availability of resources to three, or even four, where it is high. Increasing hind numbers are also associated with a reduction in the fecundity of milk hinds. In contrast, population density apparently has little effect on calf birth weight, which is closely related to weather conditions in spring. Post-natal growth, including antler size, declines as density rises.

5.4 Neonatal calf mortality does not appear to be consistently related to population density. However, mortality during the first and second winter of life rises with density, especially in stag calves.

5.5 The effects of population density on immigration and emigration are still largely unknown. The limited information available suggests that hinds seldom leave their natal area even at high density, while high deer density may reduce the rate of permanent immigration by stags.

5.6 The optimal density of deer depends on the aims of management and will vary from area to area, though within any area, the density that will yield the largest number of carcases or amount of venison per year will usually be higher than the density at which fecundity, survival and antler growth are maximised.

Where the effects of density on recruitment and survival are known, the population density most likely to satisfy specific management objectives can be calculated. Where this is not the case, the most practical approach is to proceed by trial and error.

REFERENCES

1. *Red Deer Commission Annual Report*, 1959/60. H.M.S.O., Edinburgh.
2. Fowler, C. W. (1987). 'A review of density dependence in populations of large mammals'. In: *Current Mammalogy*, ed. H. Genoways, 401−441. Plenum, New York.

3. Clutton-Brock, T. H., Iason, G. R. & Guinness, F. E. (1987). 'Sexual segregation and density-related changes in habitat use in male and female red deer'. *J. Zool.*, **211**, 275–289.

4. Clutton-Brock, T. H., Guinness, F. E. & Albon, S. D. (1982). *Red Deer: Ecology and Behavior of Two Sexes*. University of Chicago Press, Chicago.

5. Clutton-Brock, T. H., Major, M. & Guinness, F. E. (1985). 'Population regulation in male and female red deer'. *J. Anim. Ecol.*, **54**, 831–846.

6. Mitchell, B., Staines, B. W. & Welch, D. (1977). *Ecology of Red Deer: a Research Review Relevant to their Management*. Institute of Terrestrial Ecology, Cambridge.

7. Staines, B. (1978). 'The dynamics and performance of a declining population of red deer (*Cervus elaphus*)'. *J. Zool.*, **184**, 403–419.

8. Albon, S. D., Mitchell, B. & Staines, B. W. (1983). 'Fertility and body weight in female red deer: a density dependent relationship'. *J. Anim. Ecol.*, **52**, 969–980.

9. Albon, S. D. (1983). *Ecological Aspects of Growth, Reproduction and Mortality in Female Red Deer*. Ph.D. thesis, University of East Anglia.

10. Mitchell, B., McCowan, D. & Parish, T. (1986). 'Performance and population dynamics in relation to management of red deer *Cervus elaphus* at Glenfeshie, Inverness-shire, Scotland'. *Biological Conservation*, **37**, 237–267.

11. Clutton-Brock, T. H., Major, M., Albon, S. D. & Guinness, F. E. (1987). 'Early development and population dynamics in red deer I. Density-dependent effects on juvenile survival'. *J. Anim. Ecol.*, **56**, 53–68.

12. Clutton-Brock, T. H., Guinness, F. E. & Albon, S. D. (1987). 'Interactions between population density and maternal characteristics affecting fecundity and juvenile survival in red deer'. *J. Anim. Ecol.*, **56**, 857–871.

13. Clutton-Brock, T. H., Guinness, F. E. & Albon, S. D. (1984). 'Individuals and populations: the effects of social behaviour on population dynamics in deer'. *Proc. Roy. Soc. Edinb.*, **82B**, 275–290.

14. Mitchell, B. & Brown, D. (1974). 'The effects of age and body size on fertility in female red deer (*Cervus elaphus* L.)'. *Proc. Int. Congr. Game Biol.*, **11**, 89–98.

15. Albon, S. D., Mitchell, B., Huby, B. J. & Brown, D. (1986). 'Fertility in female red deer (*Cervus elaphus*): the effects of body composition, age and reproductive status'. *J. Zool. Lond.*, **209**, 447–460.

16. Clutton-Brock, T. H., Albon, S. D. & Guinness, F. E. (1985). 'Parental investment and sex differences in juvenile mortality in birds and mammals'. *Nature*, **313**, 131–133.

17. Varley, G. C. & Gradwell, G. R. (1960). 'Key factors in population studies'. *J. Anim. Ecol.*, **29**, 399–401.

18. Podoler, H. & Rogers, D. (1975). 'A new method for the identification of key factors from life-table data'. *J. Anim. Ecol.*, **44**, 85–114.

19. Houston, D. B. (1982). *The Northern Yellowstone Elk*. Macmillan, New York.

20. Taber, R. D., Raedeke, K. & McCaughran, D. A. (1982). 'Population characteristics'. In: *Elk of North America*, eds. D.W. Thomas & D. E. Towell, 279–298. Stackpole Books, Harrisberg, Pa.

21. Darling, F. F. (1937). *A Herd of Red Deer*. Oxford University Press, London.

22. Mitchell, B. & Crisp, J. M. (1981). 'Some properties of red deer (*Cervus elaphus*) at exceptionally high population density in Scotland'. *J. Zool.*, **193**, 157–169.

23. Caughley, G. (1977). *Analysis of Vertebrate Populations*. Wiley, London.

24. McNab, J. (1983). 'Wildlife management as scientific experimentation'. *Wildlife Society Bulletin*, **11**, 397–401.

6 Weather and Red Deer Populations

6.1 INTRODUCTION

The recruitment and survival of many insects and small birds is strongly affected by year to year variation in climatic conditions[1,2]. In large mammals too, these can be substantial, especially in populations living at high density or in marginal environments[3-7]. In this chapter, we describe the effects of variation in climate on body weight (Section 6.2), fecundity (Section 6.3), calving date (Section 6.4), birth weight (Section 6.5), calf mortality in summer (Section 6.6), juvenile mortality in winter (Section 6.7), adult mortality (Section 6.8) and variation in reproductive performance between cohorts (Section 6.9). The final section (Section 6.10) examines the implications of these relationships for management. The results we describe are drawn principally from studies in three different areas: Rhum, on the west coast where recruitment and survival have been monitored between 1971 and 1985; Glenfeshie, in the central Highlands where figures are available from 1966 until 1974; and some of the glens around Deeside in the eastern Highlands where figures are available from 1947 until 1964.

The effects of climatic variation on the deer might be expected to vary throughout the Highlands. As we have described in Chapter 4, deer on the west coast feed principally on grasses while deer in the east and central Highlands use heather and other dwarf shrubs to a greater extent. On the west coast, variation in annual rainfall is large, while variation in winter temperatures and snow lie is relatively small. For example, between 1961 and 1986, annual precipitation on Rhum averaged 2500 mm ranging from 1941 mm to 2999 mm. Mean January temperature was 4.4°C ranging from 1.5°C to 6.5°C and the mean number of days of snow cover was 11 and ranged from 2 to 26[8]. In contrast, at Braemar over the same period, precipitation ranged from 668 mm to 1294 mm, mean January temperature was 0.5°C, ranging from −4.7°C to 3.7°C, and the mean number of days of snow cover per year was 64 with a range of 25 to 98[8]. Results are summarised in Table 6.1.

Variation in temperature, snow cover, windspeed and rainfall affect deer populations in three main ways. First, they can increase heat loss, thus raising the animals' energy demands for maintenance activities. Calculations suggest that low temperatures combined with strong winds and rain have the greatest chilling effect, increasing heat loss by up to 100%[9]. Red deer have a higher metabolic rate than sheep or cattle and are less tolerant of low temperatures[10].

Plate 6.1 (a) Glenfeshie in winter. (Photograph: Brian Mitchell.) *(b)* Hinds in snow. (Photograph: Brian Mitchell.)

Table 6.1 Relationships between reproduction, survival and climatic factors in the central and eastern Highlands from published studies (D, Deeside, 1947–1964; GF, Glenfeshie, 1966–1974; I, Invermark, 1961–1964) compared with the west coast (Rhum, 1971–1985). All relationships show correlations across years.

Variable	West Coast (Rhum)		East and Central Highlands	
	Range	Climatic correlate	Range	Climatic correlate
Fecundity of milk hinds	29–95%	September rainfall[19]	30–82%	– (GF)[16]
Median calving date	June 2 – June 18	September rainfall[19]	June 8 – June 15	Rate of weight loss in previous winter (GF)[16]
Mean birth weight	5.9–7.3 kg	Temperature in April and May[18]	5.9–6.8 kg	Temperature in March (GF)[16]
% mortality of calves in summer	12.2–27.4	Days >5mm rainfall[19] in June	0–33%	June rainfall (I)[16]
Calves per 100 hinds in September	28–56		5–69	Snow lie in previous winter (D)[3]
Calf mortality in winter	5–45%	September rainfall[19]	2–10%	Snow lie in winter (GF)[16]
			7.8–64.1%	Duration of continuous snow cover (T)[5]
Calves per 100 hinds in May	21–42	September rainfall and Dec. – Feb. temperature	1–47	Snow lie in previous winter (D)[3]
Yearling mortality	0–34%	September rainfall[19]	Not known	–
Date of first antler shedding	March 5–March 25	January temperature	March 13 – April 8	Snow lie in winter (D)[3]
Mean larder weight in stags in autumn	84–96 kg	Temperature in previous winter[15]	84–90 kg	Snow lie in previous winter (GF)[14]
Mean larder weight of yeld hinds	54–63 kg	Soil moisture deficit[16]	55–61 kg	Snow lie in previous winter (I)[16]
			57–60 kg	Early summer rainfall (GF)[19]

Table 6.1 contd.

Variable	West Coast (Rhum)		East and Central Highlands	
	Range	Climatic correlate	Range	Climatic correlate
Rate of weight loss in winter	Not known	—	20−60 kg/day	Heather growth (GF)[16]
Adult mortality Hinds:	0−15.2%	Late summer rainfall and early winter temp.	2.3−17.1%	Duration of continuous snow cover (I)[5]
			1.5−3.5%	Snow lie in winter GF[14]
Stags:	2.5−22.0%	Early winter temperature and late summer rainfall[19]	1.3−3.0%	Snow lie in previous winter

Second, climatic variables can affect the animals' access to food supplies. In extreme cases, groups of animals can be snowed up until they starve[4]. More commonly, extensive snow cover, low temperatures or high winds can make it unprofitable for the animals to exploit a substantial part of their range.

Third, climatic variation can affect the quantity or quality of food. Low temperatures in autumn can cause an early cessation of grass growth and an increased rate of leaf mortality. In heather, too, severe frosts in winter and associated desiccation can kill or 'brown' young shoots[11]. In spring, low temperatures delay the onset of growth and can have a substantial effect on food availability in early summer. Rain, too, is important though its effects are complex. Low rainfall in spring, like low temperatures, may delay grass growth. In contrast, heavy rainfall in summer may increase growth but reduce the amount of available nutrients in leaves[12]. As we have already described (see Chapter 4), heather grows best in warm, dry summers, and where the deer feed principally on heather during the winter, wet summers are likely to be followed by low food availability in winter[13]. Finally, heavy rainfall in autumn may increase the rate of senescence in grasses either directly because of water-logged soils or indirectly because of the associated decline in sunshine.

6.2   CLIMATE, BODY WEIGHT AND CONDITION

The body weights of hinds and stags in autumn vary between years.

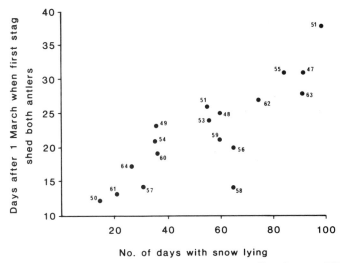

Figure 6.1 Dates of first complete antler shedding at Luibeg (eastern Highlands) plotted against the number of days of snow lie at Braemar, 1947–1964[3].

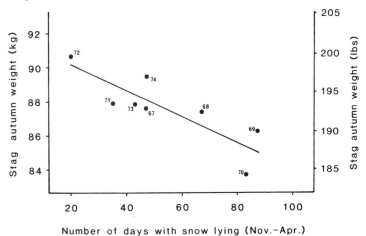

Figure 6.2 Autumn body weight of stags (7 years old) shot at Glenfeshie, 1967–1974, plotted against number of days of snow lie (November-April) the previous winter[14].

Over nine years at Glenfeshie, the average larder weight of 7-year-old stags shot in August and September ranged from 84 to 90 kg while the average weight of yeld hinds shot between late October and February ranged from 55 to 61 kg[14]. Similar variations in body weights were recorded on Rhum. Between 1959 and 1978, stag weights varied between 84 and 96 kg while hind weights ranged from 54 to 63 kg[15].

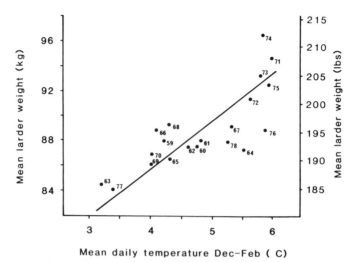

Figure 6.3 Mean adjusted larder weight for stags shot on Rhum 1959–1978 plotted against mean daily temperature in the previous winter (December-February). The weights shown are those of an average 7-year-old [15].

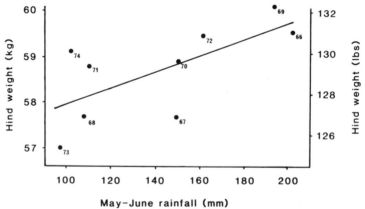

Figure 6.4 Average weight of yeld hinds shot in November at Glenfeshie plotted against rainfall in May and June, 1966–1974[16].

Winter climate has important effects on the weight and condition of stags which can persist through the following spring and summer. After cold winters when snow cover is prolonged, stags cast their antlers late (see Figure 6.1) and their body weights are lower the following autumn (Figures 6.2 and 6.3).

In hinds, which are shot later in the year, variation in body weight in winter is more closely related to summer weather conditions. At Glenfeshie, hind weights in winter between 1966 and 1974 were low

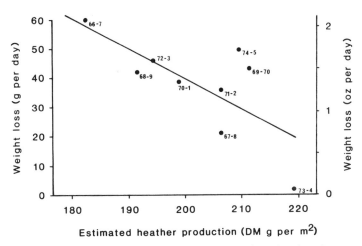

Figure 6.5 The daily weight loss of yeld hinds during the shooting season in different years at Glenfeshie, 1966–1974, plotted against estimated annual heather production[16].

after the early summer (May-June) was relatively dry (Figure 6.4), presumably because dry springs retarded grass production and food availability during the rest of the summer[16]. Even on Rhum, which has more than twice the rainfall recorded at Glenfeshie, soil moisture deficits are not uncommon and hind body weights increased in years when rainfall was higher than average[16]. However, low summer rainfall can have a beneficial effect on food availability in winter. As we have already described (see Chapter 4), heather grows best in warm, dry summers and in areas where the deer rely principally on heather during the winter, food availability may be low after wet summers. At Glenfeshie, the body weight of hinds declined more rapidly in winters following wet, cool summers when heather production had been low than after dry, warm summers when it was high (Figure 6.5).

6.3   CLIMATE AND FECUNDITY

Since differences in climate affect the weight of deer, they might be expected to affect fecundity, too. On Rhum, differences in fecundity between years were related to weather conditions in late summer and autumn. When September rainfall was high, the proportion of milk hinds calving the following year was low (see Figure 6.6) while other climatic variables showed no consistent relationships with fecundity.

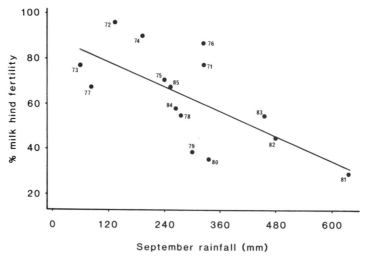

Figure 6.6 Percentage of milk hinds calving per year, 1971–1985, in the North Block of Rhum, plotted against annual precipitation in September.

The likely explanation of this relationship is that heavy September rainfall is associated with an early decline in food availability (see Chapter 4) and an increase in heat loss, reducing the rate of weight gain in milk hinds and increasing the number of animals that fail to conceive in October. At Glenfeshie, where September rainfall is typically less than half that recorded on Rhum, there was no relationship between fertility and September rainfall or any other weather variable[16].

6.4   CLIMATE, CONCEPTION AND CALVING DATES

It is sometimes suggested that climatic changes affect the timing of the rut. However, day to day changes in the activity of rutting stags can easily give a misleading impression and only systematic sampling of conception dates can provide a reliable basis for estimating changes in the timing of reproduction.

On Rhum, variation in the average date of calving is small: the median date of conception between 1971 and 1983 did not vary between years by more than four days when the effects of population density had been allowed for (see Chapter 5). At Glenfeshie, average calving date varied between years from 5 June to 15 June and was correlated with the rate at which hinds lost weight in the previous winter (Figure 6.7). Presumably, high rates of weight loss in winter were associated with light body weights the following spring and retarded fetal growth delayed calving. Similar relationships have been found in other species[17]. Other indications that winter weather can affect the date of breeding includes evidence that the estimated date of calving at Invermark was around two weeks later after the severe winter of 1962 than in previous and subsequent years[5].

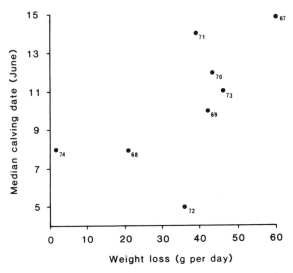

Figure 6.7 Median calving date plotted against the rate of weight loss in yeld hinds during the previous winter at Glenfeshie, 1967–1974[16].

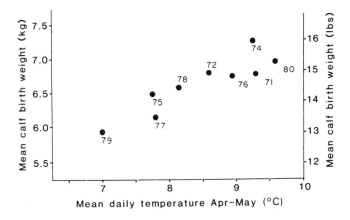

Figure 6.8 Mean birth weights of calves caught on Rhum 1971–1980, plotted against mean daily temperature in April and May in each year[18].

6.5   CLIMATE AND BIRTH WEIGHT

Spring weather can exert a strong influence on the birth weight of calves. Between 1971 and 1980, the mean birth weight of male calves born in the North Block of Rhum varied from 6.00 to 7.49 kg while the mean weight of female calves ranged from 5.94 to 6.95 kg[18]. These differences were closely related to mean daily temperature in April and May, the last two months of gestation (see Figure 6.8) and presumably occurred because low spring temperatures retarded grass growth and increased heat loss. For every 1°C increase in mean daily temperature in these months, birth weight increased by 400 g. In addition, studies at Invermark show that, following the severe winter of 1962, calves were over a kilogram lighter than in previous years[5], though, at Glenfeshie, variation in calf birth weights was uncorrelated with any indices of winter severity, except for mean daily temperature in March[16].

6.6   CLIMATE AND CALF MORTALITY IN SUMMER

In the eastern Highlands, the effects of harsh winters may persist into spring and summer. Between 1947 and 1957, ratios of calves to hinds in September on Deeside were lower after winters when snow

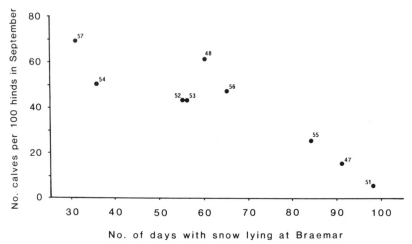

Figure 6.9   The number of calves per 100 hinds in September 1947–1957 in glens around Deeside plotted against the number of days of snow cover at Braemar the previous winter[3].

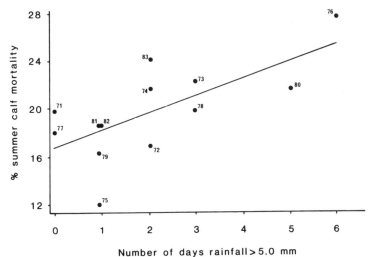

Figure 6.10   Percentage mortality of calves in their first summer on Rhum, 1971–
1983, plotted against the number of days more than 5.0 mm of rain fell in the ten-
day period after the median date of calving.

cover was prolonged (Figure 6.9). Assuming that abortion was uncommon (see Chapter 3), the most likely explanation is that cold
winters depressed birth weights and reduced the neonatal survival of
calves.

In the North Block of Rhum, summer calf mortality varied from
12.2% to 27.4% between 1971 and 1985. These differences were not
consistently related to rainfall or temperature either in spring or in
the preceding winter, nor were they correlated with population
density (see Chapter 5) or with changes in average birth weight. One
possibility is that calf mortality in summer was affected by short-
term changes in weather during the calving peak and that these were
not reflected in monthly averages. When we investigated this possibility, we found that summer calf mortality increased with the
number of days in which more than 5 mm of rain fell in the ten day
period after the median date of calving (Figure 6.10).

6.7   CLIMATE AND JUVENILE MORTALITY IN WINTER

Winter calf mortality also varies widely between years. In the central
and eastern Highlands, differences are closely related to winter
temperatures and snowfall. For example, in 1962/63, much of the
central Highlands was snow covered from mid-December until late

March. At Invermark, calf mortality rose from 9% the previous
year to 65%[5]. Similarly, between 1967 and 1974, winter calf
mortality at Glenfeshie was closely related to the duration of snow
cover (Figure 6.11). In the eastern Highlands, too, the numbers of
calves per hundred hinds were low after cold winters between 1947
and 1957 (see Figure 6.12).

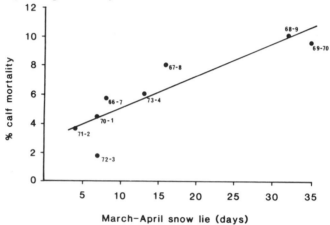

Figure 6.11   Percentage calf mortality in winter plotted against the number of days
of snow lie in March-April at Glenfeshie, 1966/67 – 1973/74[16].

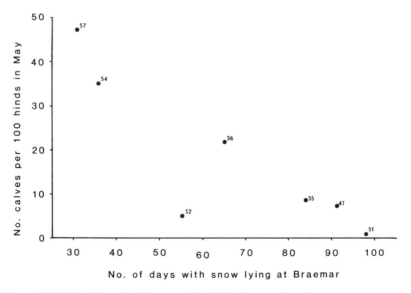

Figure 6.12   Number of calves per 100 hinds in May in glens around Deeside
plotted against the number of days snow lie at Braemar for seven years between
1947 and 1957[3].

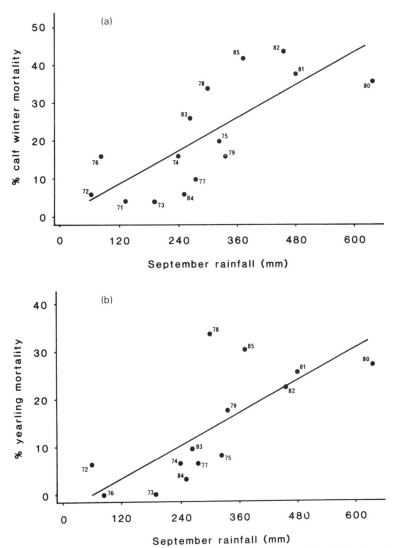

Figure 6.13 Percentage mortality in winter on Rhum 1971–1985 of (a) calves and (b) yearlings, plotted on rainfall in the previous September.

On Rhum, with its milder climate and limited snow cover, winter weather appears to be less important than rainfall in late summer and autumn[19]. In years when September rainfall was high, the over-winter mortality of calves in the North Block rose to around 40% while low September rainfall was associated with low mortality rates (see Figure 6.13a). As we described in Chapter 5, winter calf mortality increased with population density over the same period.

(a)

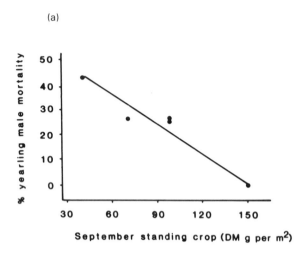

(b)

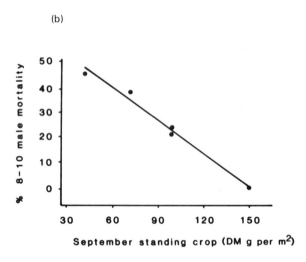

Figure 6.14 Percentage mortality in winter among (a) yearling males and (b) 8–10-year-old males plotted against the September standing crop (DM g per m^2) of live grasses and herbs on *Agrostis-Festuca* vegetation communities in the North Block, Rhum, 1981–1985. The mortality values are corrected for variation due to differences in December-February temperature[19].

However, the relationship between calf mortality and September rainfall remained when the effects of changes in density were controlled for[19]. Yearling mortality in the North Block of Rhum was also related to September rainfall, rising from $1-5\%$ after dry autumns to over 30% after wet ones (Figure 6.13b). Similar associations between autumn rainfall and juvenile mortality have been found in elk[20].

Though autumn rainfall appeared to exert a primary influence on over-winter survival of calves and yearlings on Rhum, accounting for 51% of the year to year variation in juvenile mortality, winter temperatures, too, were important. When the effects of differences in September rainfall were allowed for, calf and yearling mortality increased in years when mean daily temperatures between February and April were low[19].

Though September rainfall may increase heat loss[21], we suspect that its effects on mortality operate largely via its influence on the quantity and quality of available grass (see Section 6.1). An early cessation of grass growth combined with rapid leaf senescense is likely to lead to reduced food availability in winter (Chapter 4) and lower weight gain in the deer during autumn. After wet Septembers the low standing crop of live grasses and herbs was associated with increased mortality in male yearlings and 8–10-year-olds (Figure 6.14(a)).

6.8 CLIMATE AND ADULT MORTALITY

Like calf mortality (see above) variation in adult mortality in the central and eastern Highlands is closely related to winter snow lie. Between 1947 and 1964 the number of animals found dead each year in Upper Mar forest, Deeside was closely related to the number of days of snow lie at Braemar[3] (see Figure 6.15). Similarly, when the effects of population density on hind mortality were allowed for, differences at Glenfeshie were consistently related to late winter snow lie[16], although stag mortality was related to snow lie in the *previous* winter (Figure 6.16), possibly because the previous winter's snow lie affected autumn weight (see Figure 6.2) and hence the condition of stags at the onset of the rut.

On Rhum, too, adult mortality was related to winter temperatures[22]. Between 1959 and 1976 the total number of animals found dead on the island in spring ranged from less than 20

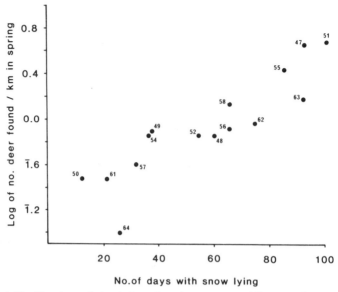

Figure 6.15 Number of dead deer found per square kilometre in Upper Mar forest, compared with number of days with snow lying at Braemar, 1947–1964[3].

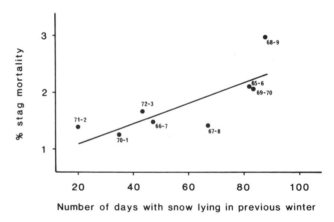

Figure 6.16 Percentage stag mortality at Glenfeshie between 1966 and 1974 plotted against number of days snow lie in the previous winter[14].

after mild winters to over 80 after cold ones (see Figure 6.17). More recent work in the North Block of Rhum indicates that hind mortality was related primarily to late summer rainfall and, secondarily, to temperature in early winter (November/December)

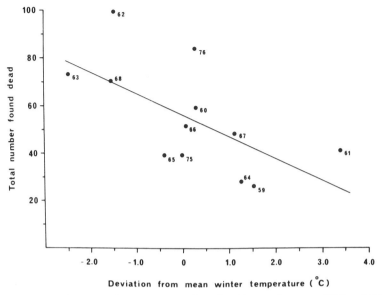

Figure 6.17 Spring mortality counts on Rhum for 12 years between 1959 and 1976 plotted against the sum of the deviations from the mean daily temperature of each of the months January-March in the ratio (1/2:1:1). Numbers beside each point show the year[22].

(Figure 6.18). Together, these variables accounted for 72% of the annual variation in hind mortality[19]. Stag mortality, in contrast, was more closely related to temperature in November and December than to August-September rainfall and together these two variables account for 49% of the variance between years[19]. However, standing crop in autumn may also be important (see Figure 6.14(b)).

6.9 CLIMATE AND DIFFERENCES IN REPRODUCTIVE PERFORMANCE BETWEEN COHORTS

As we have described in Section 6.5, average calf birth weights in the North Block of Rhum varied widely between years in relation to spring temperatures. Although these differences were not closely related to the immediate survival of calves, they were closely correlated with their reproductive performance as adults[23]. Hinds born below average weight remained below average weight as adults[24] and produced light calves throughout the whole of their

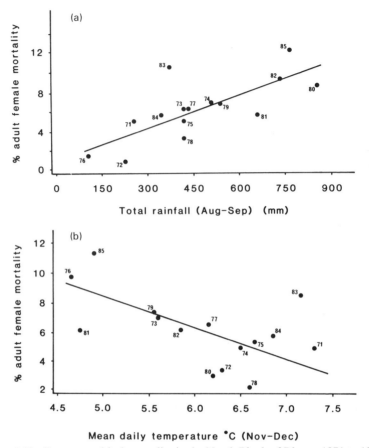

Figure 6.18 Percentage hind mortality in the North Block of Rhum, 1971 to 1985, plotted against (a) August-September rainfall and (b) November-December temperature. In each case the plot is corrected for the effects of the other variable.

lives. These differences were substantial: the average weight of calves produced over their lifetime by members of cohorts born between 1970 and 1979 varied by 40%, ranging from 5.0 kg to more than 7.0 kg (see Figure 6.19).

The chances that a calf will survive its first two winters are closely related to its birth weight (see Chapters 3 and 5). As might be expected, cohorts of hinds that produced light calves showed consistently high levels of calf loss, and offspring survival during the first two years of life varied between cohorts of mothers from as little as 10% to over 60% (Figure 6.20).

The existence of relationships between the birth weight of cohorts and the birth weight and survival of their progeny does not

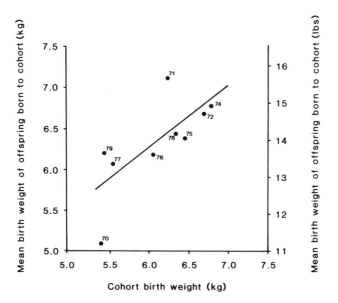

Figure 6.19   Mean offspring birth weight calculated across hinds belonging to different cohorts on Rhum and plotted against the mean birth weight of the cohort to which they belonged[23]. To calculate the mean birth weight of calves born to each cohort, we calculated the mean weight of all calves produced by each hind born between 1970 and 1979 over the rest of her lifespan. The mean birth weight of calves born to the cohort was the mean of these values for individual hinds in each cohort.

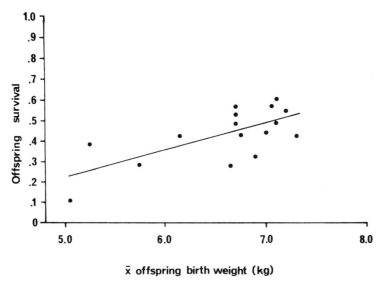

Figure 6.20   Mean survival of offspring between birth and two years calculated across hinds belonging to different cohorts on Rhum and plotted against the mean birth weight of offspring born to those cohorts of hinds[23].

necessarily mean that birth weight affects an animal's adult size and reproductive performance directly. It may be that annual variation in birth weight merely reflects changes in the milk yield of hinds which, in turn, affect the growth and eventual reproductive performance of their calves. However, these results clearly show that cohorts of deer that are born after late springs are likely to show consistently poor reproductive performance over the rest of their lives. Though these effects have so far been investigated only in the North Block of Rhum, there is no evidence that they are closely related to population density and we would expect them to be even more pronounced in the colder climate of the central and eastern Highlands. In fact, similar differences have been found between cohorts in other vertebrates[25] and they may prove to be a common feature of population dynamics.

6.10   IMPLICATIONS FOR MANAGEMENT

The strong effects of variation in weather on growth, recruitment and survival in Highland red deer have four main implications for management. First, they suggest that any measures which can be taken to increase the availability of food at the beginning of the winter or in spring or heat retention by animals in winter may have substantial effects on recruitment and survival. As we described in Chapter 4, the improvement of low ground by draining, liming or re-seeding and moderate burning of hill pastures may increase the quality and abundance of food available to deer in spring and autumn. Shelter belts may help to reduce heat loss in winter and thus to reduce winter mortality, especially in stags which appear to be more susceptible to low winter temperatures than hinds (see also Chapter 2).

Second, they suggest that natural mortality will never be entirely eliminated by culling, even where this holds deer numbers below the level that the environment can support. Results for Rhum suggest that there is not always a close relationship between culling rate and the proportion of adults that die in winter (see Chapter 8).

Third, the close relationship between climatic factors, recruitment and survival indicates that either consistent changes in weather or runs of good or bad years occurring by chance are likely to affect the potential culling rate that populations can sustain. Where a run of good or bad years produces a series of cohorts of hinds with superior or inferior breeding success, average calf production and, consequently, the maximum yield that populations can sustain is likely to vary as these cohorts pass through their lifespans (see Chapter 8). For example, our calculations suggest that during the late sixties and early seventies, when weather conditions were favourable, the hind population of Rhum could have sustained an annual cull of 14% whereas this probably fell to around 10% in the late seventies and eighties due to wetter autumns and colder winters.

Finally, the consistent differences in breeding success which exist between cohorts of hinds emphasize the potential benefits of selective culling. The elimination of animals from poor cohorts should help to raise the average breeding success of the population and the rate of culling that it can sustain.

6.11 SUMMARY

6.1   Changes in annual climate have an important influence on reproduction and survival in Highland red deer. The relative importance of variation in rainfall and winter temperature varies between the west coast and the Central Highlands. On the west coast, rainfall is very variable and winters are usually mild, while in the East and Central Highlands, rainfall is lower but the duration of snow cover shows large differences between years. As might be expected, survival and recruitment are best predicted by rainfall on the west coast and by snow cover in the East and Central Highlands.

6.2   The body weights and condition of both sexes are affected by weather conditions. The condition of stags in spring, measured by the date of antler casting, and their weight the following autumn are both related to winter temperatures and snow cover. In contrast, the weight of hinds in November and December varies in relation to summer rainfall and the severity of the previous winter.

6.3–6.5 Variation in climate also affects fecundity and calving rate. In the North Block of Rhum, the fecundity of milk hinds is low when September rainfall is high, the timing of conception varies little and birth weights are closely related to temperature in April and May, the last two months of gestation. At Glenfeshie, calving dates vary with the weight loss of hinds in the previous winter and are late after harsh winters.

6.6–6.8 Climatic variation also affects mortality. In the Central and Eastern Highlands, calf mortality during winter is high in years with heavy snow fall, while on Rhum it is most closely associated with rainfall in autumn and with winter temperature. The mortality of calves in summer differs between years in relation to rainfall during the peak calving period.

The mortality of adults of both sexes is most closely related to snow cover in winter in the Central and Eastern Highlands. On Rhum, stag mortality is related primarily to winter temperature while hind mortality varies with autumn rainfall and, secondarily, with winter temperature.

6.9   Pronounced differences in reproductive performance exist between cohorts of hinds. These are related to their average birth weight and to spring temperature in their year of birth.

6.10 The strong effects of weather on recruitment, survival and breeding success indicate that either consistent changes in climate or chance runs of good or bad years can have an important influence on the maximum culling rate that populations can sustain. Improvement of the quality or quantity of food available to the deer, especially in early winter and spring, or any changes which reduce energy expenditure during the winter may have a substantial effect on recruitment and survival.

REFERENCES

1. Andrewartha, H. G. & Birch, L. C. (1954). *The Distribution and Abundance of Animals*. University of Chicago Press, Chicago.
2. Lack, D. (1966). *Population Studies of Birds*. Oxford University Press, Oxford.
3. Watson, A. (1971). 'Climate and the antler-shedding and performance of red deer in North-east Scotland'. *J. Appl. Ecol.*, **8**, 53–68.
4. Mitchell, B. & Staines, B. W. (1976). 'An example of natural winter mortality in Scottish red deer'. *Deer*, **3**, 549–552.
5. Mitchell, B. (1984). 'Some effects of the severe winter of 1962/63 on red deer hinds and calves in N.E. Scotland'. *Deer*, **6**, 81–84.
6. Sobanskii, G. G. (1979). 'Selective elimination in the Siberian stag population in the Altais as a result of the early winter of 1976/77'. *Soviet Journal of Ecology*, **10**, 78–80. (Translated from Russian, Consultants Bureau, New York.)
7. Picton, H. D. (1984). 'Climate and the prediction of reproduction of three ungulate species'. *J. Appl. Ecol.*, **21**, 869–879.
8. *Monthly Weather Records*, Metereological Office, H.M.S.O., London.
9. Grace, J. & Easterbee, N. (1979). 'The natural shelter for red deer (*Cervus elaphus*) in a Scottish glen'. *J. Appl. Ecol.*, **16**, 37–48.
10. Simpson, A., Webster, A. J. F., Smith, J. S. & Simpson, C. A. (1978). 'Energy and nitrogen metabolism of red deer (*Cervus elaphus*) in cold environments: a comparison with cattle and sheep'. *Comp. Biochem. Physiol.*, **60**, 251–256.
11. Watson, A., Miller, G. R. & Green, H. W. (1966). 'Winter browning of heather (*Calluna vulgaris*) and other moorland plants'. *Trans. Bot. Soc. Edinb.*, **40**, 195–203.

12. Deinum, B. (1984). 'Chemical composition and nutritive value of herbage in relation to climate'. In: Riley, H. & Skjelvag, A. O. (eds). *The Impact of Climate on Grass Production and Quality*, 338–350. Proc. 10th General Meeting of the European Grassland Federation, As, Norway.

13. Miller, G. R. (1979). 'Quantity and quality of the annual production of shrubs and flowers by *Calluna vulgaris* in North-east Scotland'. *J. Ecol.*, **67**, 109–129.

14. Mitchell, B., unpublished.

15. Clutton-Brock, T. H. & Albon, S. D. (1983). 'Climatic variation and body weight of red deer'. *J. Wildlife Mgmt*, **47**, 1197–1201.

16. Albon, S. D. (1983). *Ecological Aspects of Growth, Reproduction and Mortality in Female Red Deer*. Ph.D. thesis, University of East Anglia.

17. Thorne, E. T., Dean, R. E. & Hepworth, W. G. (1976). 'Nutrition during gestation in relation to successful reproduction in elk'. *J. Wildl. Mgmt.*, **40**, 330–335.

18. Albon, S. D., Guinness, F. E. & Clutton-Brock, T. H. (1983). 'The influence of climatic variation on the birth weights of red deer calves'. *J. Zool.*, **200**, 295–297.

19. Albon, S. D. & Clutton-Brock, T. H. (1988). 'Temporal variation in climate and the population dynamics of red deer in Scotland'. In: *Ecological Change in the Uplands*, ed. M. B. Usher & D. Thompson, pp. 93–107. British Ecological Symposium, Blackwells, Oxford.

20. Sauer, J. R. & Boyce, M. S. (1983). 'Density dependence and survival of elk in Northwestern Wyoming'. *J. Wildl. Mgmt.*, **47**, 31–37.

21. Beddington, J. R. (1973). *The Exploitation of Red Deer Cervus elaphus L. in Scotland*. Ph.D. thesis, University of Edinburgh.

22. Clutton-Brock, T.H. & Albon, S.D. (1982). 'Winter mortality in Red deer (*Cervus elaphus*)'. *J. Zool. Lond.*, **198**, 515–519.

23. Albon, S. D., Clutton-Brock, T. H. & Guinness, F. E. (1987). 'Early development and population dynamics in red deer II. Density-independent effects and cohort variation'. *J. Anim. Ecol.*, **56**, 69–82.

24. Clutton-Brock, T. H., Albon, S. D. & Guinness, F. E. (1988). 'Reproductive success in red deer'. In: *Reproductive Success*, ed. T. H. Clutton-Brock, pp. 325–343. University of Chicago Press, Chicago.

25. Craig, J. F. (1980). 'Growth and production of the 1955 to 1972 cohorts of perch, *Perca fluviatilis* L. in Windermere'. *J. Animal Ecology*, **49**, 291–316.

7 Red Deer in Commerical Forests

7.1 INTRODUCTION

About 13% of Scotland is now covered by commercial forests and, in recent years, over 30,000 ha have been planted per year[1, 2]. It is estimated that a further 1.7 million ha could be forested. Sitka spruce (*Picea sitchensis*) predominates but Norway spruce (*Picea abies*), lodgepole pine (*Pinus contorta*), larch (*Larix*) and Scots pine (*Pinus sylvestris*) are also common.

Estimates of the number of deer in forestry populations range from 27,000[2] to 50,000[3]. Red deer can cause substantial damage to plantations. Some are fenced against deer but many are not and have gradually been colonized by red deer over the last 20–30 years[4] or are subject to regular winter incursions. In addition, fencing rarely excludes red deer totally and many fenced plantations now support resident or semi-resident populations[2]. Because of the problems of studying forest-dwelling deer, their ecology is less well-known than that of populations living on the open hill. However, recent research on forest-dwelling populations throughout Scotland[2,5] especially in Galloway[2,6] and at Glenbranter and Glen Cripesdale in Argyll[2,7,8,9], and at Grizedale in the North of England[10], are helping to fill this gap. In this chapter, we describe what is known of the population density growth (Section 7.2) and population dynamics (Section 7.3), habitat use and ranging behaviour (Section 7.4) of Scottish red deer populations living in commercial forests. Section 7.5 briefly reviews studies of their impact on their habitat while Section 7.6 reviews research on their interactions with the two other deer species that colonize plantations in the Highlands: roe (*Capreolus capreolus*) and sika deer (*Cervus nippon*). The last section examines some of the implications of the presence of forest-dwelling deer populations for the management of Highland populations as a whole.

7.2 POPULATION DENSITY

It is seldom possible to count deer living in forestry plantations directly and subjective estimates consistently underestimate actual densities, in some cases by more than a factor of ten. Most attempts to estimate population density in commercial forests rely either on pellet counts[2,7,11,12] or on counts of limited areas within the forest from vantage points[2,4]. Both techniques have their problems[2]. Scatters of pellets may differ in visibility or decomposition rate

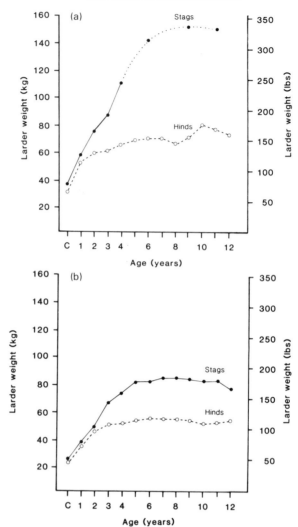

Figure 7.1 Mean larder weights of stags (●) and hinds (o) shot at (a) Grizedale Forest in Cumbria [10] in winter between 1969–1977 and (b) at Glenfeshie, Inverness-shire [16] in late summer/early autumn between 1966–1973.

between habitats and their local distribution may reflect the distribution of areas used by the deer to rest rather than feed[2]. Counts from vantage points may underestimate deer numbers and the accuracy of estimates based on these counts will be influenced by sampling methodology[2,13].

Existing estimates of red deer numbers in commercial forests in the Highlands suggest that population density varies over much the same range as on the open hill, running from less than 5 animals per square kilometre to over 20 per square kilometre[2,4,5]. Calf/hind ratios are typically higher in forestry populations than on the open hill (see below) but it is not yet known whether the ratio of stags to hinds is consistently higher.

Total red deer density varies with the growth stage of the forest and is usually low during the period of initial forest establishment when trees are less than 1 metre tall, higher during the pre-thicket stage, when tree height is between 1 and 3 metres, and close to their peak at the late pre-thicket and thicket stages when trees have grown to 3–10 metres where there are many open areas within or adjacent to the forest[14,15]. Numbers commonly decline during the pole stage, when trees reach their final height and ground vegetation is usually sparse. Population density may increase in subsequent rotations when a variety of different habitat types are available to the deer.

7.3 GROWTH AND REPRODUCTIVE PERFORMANCE

Red deer resident in forestry plantations can achieve much larger sizes and higher body weights than those living on the open hill. For example at Grizedale Forest in Cumbria[10] most hinds achieve a (larder) weight of 65-75 kg while stags weigh between 145 and 155 kg (see Figure 7.1). Average hind weights are thus around 34% heavier than on Rhum and 38% heavier than at Glenfeshie while stags were 67% and 73% heavier respectively. The tendency for improvements in habitat to affect male weight more than female weight is found in many other mammals where males are larger than females[17].

The fecundity of hinds living in forestry is often higher than on the open hill especially in forest-dwelling populations at relatively low density[2]. At Grizedale, around 65% of yearlings were pregnant and nearly 100% of older hinds[10]. Fertility of mature hinds varies with population density among Scottish forests, ranging from 100% in low density populations to 60% in populations at high density[12]. As on the open hill, the probability that a hind is fertile increases with her weight, but lactating hinds appear to conceive at lower weights than non-lactating ones[2]. Yearling pregnancy rates also show marked differences[2], varying from less than 10% in high density populations to nearly 100% in low density ones though, especially at low density, they are consistently higher than on the open hill (Figure 7.2). Twinning is very rare (one case in 140

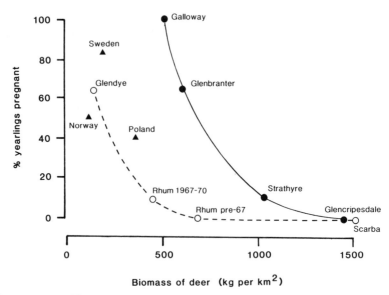

Figure 7.2 Fertility of yearling red deer in Scottish and continental populations[5]. Note that for a given biomass of deer, fertility rates are consistently higher in forest-living (●) populations than in those inhabiting the open-hill (○).

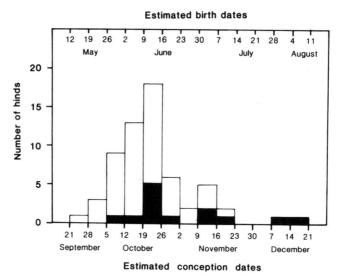

Figure 7.3 Distribution of conception and parturition dates at Grizedale, Cumbria[10]. □ Adults; ■ Yearlings.

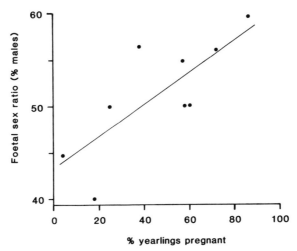

Figure 7.4 Foetal sex ratios (% male) from samples of hinds culled in nine different Scottish commercial forests, plotted against the proportion of yearlings in the population that were pregnant[2].

pregnancies examined from Grizedale) but may be slightly more frequent than on the open hill[2,10]. These figures suggest that many forest living populations have a potential birth rate approaching 70 calves per 100 hinds[5].

The little evidence that is available suggests that conception and birth dates in forest living populations are similar to those on the hill (see Figure 7.3). Overall, birth sex ratios approximate to 50:50 though Ratcliffe[2] has found a consistent tendency for the sex ratio of foetuses to rise in favour of males in populations showing high reproductive performance, estimated from the proportion of yearlings pregnant (Figure 7.4). Calf mortality is probably lower than in open hill populations and may be around 10%[4,5]. Spring and winter counts at Glenbranter give an average of 48 calves per 100 hinds while similar counts in Galloway suggest a ratio of 55 calves per 100 hinds.

The high fecundity and low juvenile mortality of forest-dwelling red deer suggest that relatively high culling rates may be necessary to control population size. For example, calculations for red deer in Galloway suggest that an annual cull of 18−20% is necessary to stabilize density[2].

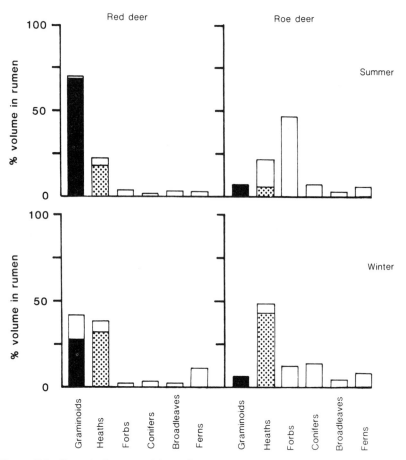

Figure 7.5 Botanical composition of rumen samples from red and roe deer at Glenbranter (% volume of total rumen contents). Summer = April-October; winter = late October-March. = ■ grasses; = ▨ Calluna.[7].

7.4 HABITAT PREFERENCES AND FEEDING ECOLOGY

Habitat use in forest-living deer has been studied in detail only at Glenbranter, Argyll. Here, a large area of forest covering two main glen systems was planted between 1922 and 1939[18]. Contrary to present day practice, Sitka spruce was planted on the lower slopes with Norway spruce at higher elevations. Felling and partial replanting, together with attacks by voles, wind damage and poor growth in some areas have led to a mosaic of different age classes which is representative of British forests in the second or subsequent planting rotation (see Plate 7.1)[9]. Both red deer and roe deer use the forest at densities of 9–10 animals per square kilometre[7].

Plate 7.1   Glenbranter Forest, Argyll, showing Sitka spruce in the establishment phase. (Photograph: B. W. Staines.)

Habitat use at Glenbranter has been studied by the analysis of pellet counts[2,7,11] and by observation combined with radio-tracking[8,9,19,20]. Both techniques showed that forest-living deer spent a disproportionate amount of time in rides and clearings within the forest. Red deer use is highest in areas of thicket and pre-thicket which are interspersed with rides, glades and other open areas where the deer feed[2]. Pellet count techniques showed strong selection for the establishment (or re-stocking) stages of the forest cycle, followed by pre-thicket and thicket[7] while radio-tracking showed selection against establishment and higher preferences for pre-thicket and poll[8,9]. Differences in estimates of the use of establishing forest may have been caused by the problems of finding animals to radio track in these areas which mostly lay in the more remote parts of the glen, while the relatively heavy use of pole and thicket revealed by radio-tracking may have been misleading since it was not possible to distinguish between the use of forest blocks and the use of rides or glades within them[8]. Though sample sizes were small, radio-tracking suggested that males spent a higher proportion

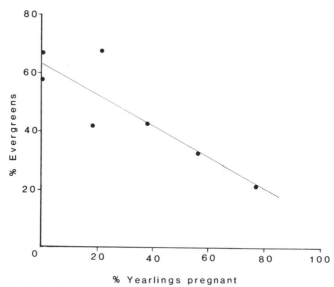

Figure 7.6 Variation in fertility (% of yearlings pregnant) in relation to differences in the proportion of evergreens (mostly heather) in the diet of red deer shot in seven different commerical forests in Scotland[2].

of their time in older stands, in high altitude plantations and on surrounding areas of open hill ground than did females[8].

Habitat use varied throughout the day. Hinds selected areas with more rides to a greater extent during the day and at dusk than at night or dawn while more open areas, including plantations in the establishment phase, were more frequently used at night[8,9]. Greater use of open areas during the night and use of thicker cover by day has been recorded in Scandinavia[21] and may be a response to shooting pressure[22].

The ranges of hinds (406—1008 ha) were similar to those on Rhum, but smaller than in the eastern Highlands (see Chapter 4) and declined with the proportion of preferred habitat within the range[8,9]. There was no evidence of seasonal shifts in range use or of seasonal variation in range size. As on Rhum, many males appeared to disperse from their natal area by about 3 years of age.

Gross activity patterns in red deer at Glenbranter were similar in most respects to those of red deer on Rhum[9]. Radio-tracked animals spent 14 hours per day active, compared to 11—12 hours grazing and a further 1—2 hours standing or moving on Rhum. Activity peaked at dawn and dusk[9,19]. However, unlike red deer on Rhum, there was no tendency for the amount of time spent active to increase in winter[9].

Analysis of rumen contents from Glenbranter showed that, in summer, the diet of the deer consisted primarily of grass and heather, with smaller amounts of heathers, forbs, conifers, broad-leaved trees or shrubs and ferns while, in winter, the proportion of heather in the diet increased (see Figure 7.5). In Scottish forests where palatable grasses are in short supply and red deer eat a high proportion of evergreens (mostly heather) in autumn, rumen fill is high but levels of nitrogen and ammonia in the rumen are low and fertility is depressed (see Figure 7.6).

7.5   IMPACT ON FORESTS

The extent to which browsing damages trees usually varies in relation to their age and size. Mature trees withstand severe browsing of lower shoots without serious damage, while heavy browsing of younger trees can lead to loss of growth increment, mis-shapen growth, permanent size reduction or even to the failure of parts of the plantation[16,23]. Severity of damage is related to whether or not the leading shoot is removed, to the amount of shoot taken and to the frequency of browsing[24-26]. Even where browse constitutes a relatively small proportion of their diet, red deer can still have a substantial impact on the trees and shrubs around them. At Glenbranter, browsing of Sitka spruce peaked in late winter and early summer and was lowest between June and August[7]. Trees were most likely to have their leaders browsed when they were between 30 and 60 cm high while the leaders of trees taller than 80 cm were relatively safe from browsing. Of 30–60 cm trees, between 40% and 70% had their leaders browsed each year though this varied widely between sites. However, more than 50% of damaged trees grew new leaders in that following season[7]

Browsing by red deer has been studied in a variety of other forests throughout Europe[16]. Preferences for particular tree species are marked and are largely stable across habitats: aspen (*Populus tremula*) and willow (*Salix* spp.) are always highly preferred while alder (*Alnus glutinosa*), birch (*Betula* spp.) and Sitka spruce usually have relatively low preference ratings (see Table 7.1). In some areas, Scots pine is also seldom browsed and in plantations in the northern Highlands this was less affected by browsing than Sitka spruce or lodgepole pine[32,33].

Bark stripping by red deer is also common. Norway spruce is

Table 7.1 Ranking orders of browse preferences by red deer in six different areas[(from 16)]

Author	Sablina[27]	Dzieciolowski[28]	Bobek, Weiner Zielinski[29]*	Ueckermann[30]	Ahlen[21]	Chard[31]
Area	White Russia	Poland	Poland	West Germany	S. Sweden	N.W. England
Highly preferred	*Salix* *Populus tremula* *Fraxinus* *Quercus*	*Quercus petraea* *Salix caprea* *Sorbus aucuparia* *Corylus*	*Populus tremula* *Salix caprea* *Frangula alnus*	*Populus tremula* *Quercus borealis* *Abies* *Acer platanoides* *Fraxinus* *Quercus*	*Fraxinus* *Salix* *Frangula alnus*	*Juniperus* *Quercus borealis* *Pinus contorta* *Picea abies*
Preferred	*Sorbus aucuparia* *Betula*	*Acer platanoides* *Carpinus* *Prunus serotina* *Frangula alnus*	*Quercus robur*	*Pinus sylvestris* *Picea abies* *Fagus* *Pseudotsuga* *Larix*	*Betula*	*Larix* *Acer pseudo-platanus* *Pinus sylvestris* *Quercus* *Betula*
Seldom or never browsed	*Tilia* *Carpinus*	*Pinus sylvestris* *Juniperus*	*Tilia cordata* *Carpinus* *Betula*	*Picea sitchensis* *Alnus* *Betula*	*Alnus*	*Picea sitchensis* *Fagus sylvatica* *Alnus glutinosa*

*Includes roe deer.

generally more vulnerable than Sitka in Scotland but outbreaks of severe stripping of Sitka can occur[16]. At Glenbranter, Sitka spruce became vulnerable to bark stripping when their trunks exceeded 10 cm in girth and they were at least 8 years old[7]. In older stands, the deer selected smaller trunks whereas in pre-thicket and thicket stages they selected the larger trees. In Sitka stands of 10–35 years old, around 1% of trees were damaged yearly, though over 5% of trees showed signs of bark stripping in some areas.

Bark stripping also occurs in many continental forests[30,34,35], though in some countries, such as Bulgaria, it is almost unknown[36]. The susceptibility of different species to bark stripping is generally similar to their susceptibility to browsing (see Table 7.2) though silver fir suffers comparatively little from bark stripping while Norway spruce is highly susceptible. Differences appear to be related to the thickness, hardness and smoothness of the bark, the amount of protection afforded by the lower branches and to the strength of the animals' preference for the species[16]. Bark is typically taken from between 0.75–1.25 m above ground level but is sometimes taken as high as 1.7 m[25,37].

Some tree species, like beech (*Fagus sylvatica*), are most commonly damaged in summer when the sap is rising and the cambium is active[37], while conifers are most likely to be bark-stripped in winter[30,41,42]. In some cases, it is also reported that stands which have recently been thinned are subject to more intensive stripping while plantations appear to be more susceptible than natural woodlands[42,43].

Like browsing, bark stripping can lead to defects in the timber and can increase the chance of attack by bacteria or fungi entering through the wound while, in extreme cases, it can even kill the tree[23,41,44]. In Argyll, Maxwell[45] estimated that stripping of pole-stage trees caused them to lose 40% in volume increment while in other forests, too, stripping can cause substantial reductions in commercial yield[46]. As with browsing, the severity of effects varies with species and size of tree[34,41,42]. Norway spruce, in particular, can be severely damaged though selective thinning can reduce the effects of stripping on commercial yield, while Douglas fir, silver fir and lime are more resistant to damage[16,47,48].

Like North American elk[49-51], red deer can modify the composition of woodland[16]. Throughout the Highlands, browse is so scarce on the open hill that saplings of a wide variety of species are regularly browsed and regeneration is often totally prevented (see

Table 7.2 Ranking order of susceptibilities to bark stripping by red deer from six different areas.

Author	Sablina[27]	Muller[37]	Ueckermann[30,38]	Strandgaard[39]	McIntyre[40]	Pellew[41]
Area	White Russia	East Germany	West Germany	Denmark	Galloway	N.W. England
Highly susceptible	*Salix* *Fraxinus*	*Picea abies* *Fraxinus* *Pseudotsuga*	*Picea abies* *Fraxinus* *Salix* *Populus*	*Picea abies* *Pinus contorta* *Pinus mugo*	*Pinus contorta* *Pinus sylvestris*	*Pinus contorta* *Pinus sylvestris* *Picea abies*
Moderately susceptible	*Alnus incana* *Sorbus aucuparia* *Quercus* *Pinus sylvestris* *Picea abies* *Betula*	*Fagus* *Abies* *Pinus sylvestris* *Acer*	*Pseudotsuga* *Tilia* *Pinus sylvestris* *Fagus* *Larix* *Sorbus aucuparia* *Acer pseudo-platanus*	*Larix* *Pseudotsuga* *Picea sitchensis* *Abies*	*Larix* *Picea abies*	*Pseudotsuga* *Larix (Japanese)* *Larix decidua*
Seldom affected	*Tilia* *Carpinus*	*Quercus*	*Abies* *Quercus* *Alnus* *Betula*		*Picea sitchensis*	*Picea sitchensis*

Chapter 4). The comparative scarcity of aspen, rowan and willow throughout the Highlands probably reflects a combination of intense browsing pressure and burning in the past. In continental Europe, too, preferred species like ash, silver fir and beech can be reduced in number or replaced by more resistant species[52,53]. The ground vegetation of Scottish woodlands also can be affected by browsing[16]. In shady conditions, *Vaccinium myrtillus* and *V. vitis-idaea* tend to replace *Calluna*[54] and moderate browsing pressure appears to encourage this succession. However, where browsing pressure is high, *Vaccinium* is in turn eliminated and replaced by grassy communities dominated by *Deschampsia flexuosa* and bryophytes[16].

Foresters have devoted considerable time and effort to attempts to control browsing and bark stripping, with variable success[23]. In northern and western Scotland, fencing plantations is common and can play an important role in protecting the growing trees though in southern and western Scotland, it is less popular because the numbers of deer living on the open hill are lower. In many areas, fencing represents a temporary measure, for red deer will usually penetrate and colonize substantial forests, either by walking over the top of fences during periods of heavy snowfall or by finding holes in or under the wire. An alternative approach is to permit colonization but to control numbers by shooting or temporary exclosure[55,56]. However, even where forests have been designed to facilitate deer control, it can be difficult to kill enough animals to control population size[2].

Other approaches to limiting damage include the protection of trees with chemical repellants[23,57,58] or sheets of polythene or netting[30], scarification of bark (inducing resin flow and making the bark rough and difficult to peel)[30,39,59] and scaring deer with optical, acoustic or olfactory devices, including the dung of carnivores[60,61]. All these methods can serve to reduce damage temporarily or even permanently but, in many areas, they are either ineffective or uneconomic for use in protecting large plantations.

Finally, in parts of eastern and central Europe, artificial food is provided with the aim of reducing browsing or bark stripping. This can lead to substantial reductions in damage[30,39,62] but its effects depend on the type of forest and the distribution of artificial food. In some cases, the provision of food may even increase damage to trees by concentrating deer in particular areas of the forest or by increasing their need for roughage to balance the high quality food provided[43,63,64].

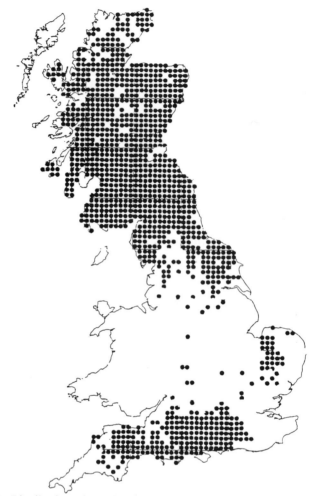

Figure 7.7   Distribution of roe deer in Britain.

7.6 INTERACTIONS WITH ROE AND SIKA DEER

In many Scottish forests, red deer share their habitat with two other cervids: the indigenous roe deer (*Capreolus capreolus*) and the introduced sika deer (*Cervus nippon*). After the original destruction of most of Scotland's ancient forests (see Chapter 1), roe deer did not colonize the open hill to the same extent as red deer, but viable populations persisted in many remaining areas of woodland. In this century, their range has expanded with the spread of commercial forestry in the Highlands and many Scottish forests now support substantial roe deer populations (see Figure 7.7).

To what extent do roe deer compete with red deer for resources? Research at Glenbranter provides an opportunity to compare the habitat use and feeding ecology of red deer and roe in the same forest environment[7,9]. Densities of the two species were similar, lying between 9 and 10 animals per square kilometre. Pellet group counts showed that both selected similar areas of habitat, preferring rides and open areas adjacent to planted ground. Roe appeared to be more selective than red in their use of habitat and used areas of pre-thicket more and areas of thicket less[7]. In contrast, red deer made more use of the central portions of pole and high canopy forest and were more frequently seen further from the edge of cover at night[9].

Differences in diet between the two species were more pronounced than in habitat use. In summer, red deer fed mainly on grasses, while roe ate a higher proportion of forbs and blaeberry (see Figure 7.5). In winter, diet overlap increased and both species fed extensively on *Calluna*, which constituted 30% of rumen volume in red deer and around 40% in roe deer[7]. Red deer fed relatively more on spruce than roe deer in early summer while in autumn and early winter the situation was reversed. At Glenbranter where both species are regularly culled, competition between red deer and roe appears to be slight and differences in habitat use between the two species are unlikely to be caused by competitive exclusion[9,see also refs 65,66].

Between 1879 and 1910, sika deer escaped from several Scottish deer parks and were intentionaly released in at least two sites in the Highlands (Rosehall, in Sutherland, and Aldourie, Inverness-shire)[67]. All feral populations in Scotland are thought to be derived from Japanese stock, belonging to the relatively small subspecies, *Cervus nippon nippon*[67,68,69]. Since 1930, Scottish sika populations have extended their range considerably (Figure 7.8) and their rate of spread is now probably increasing[67]. No reliable estimates of their population density in Scotland are yet available but, in Germany, densities of 3–4 sika per square kilometre have been reported in mixed deciduous and coniferous forests[70,71]. Unlike red deer, sika are largely confined to areas of woodland and forestry plantations, where they may cause as much damage as red deer[67,72]. Their diet appears to be similar to that of red deer, though they may have a better capacity to digest fibrous food[73].

Some research in New Zealand suggests that sika may be able to out-compete red deer[74,75]. However, in Scotland, hybridization between sika and red deer is likely to pose a more important problem

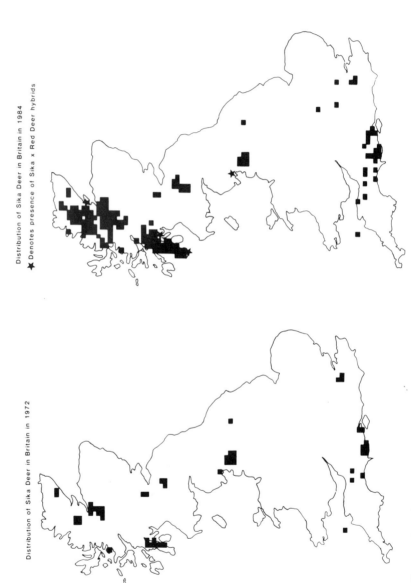

Figure 7.8 Distribution of Sika deer in Britain in (a) 1972 and (b) 1984 (from Ratcliffe, 1987 Mammal Review, 17[67]).

than competition. Hybrids are still uncommon in the Highlands[67] and some authorities suggest that, where red deer and Japanese sika are sympatric, both populations may maintain their genetic integrity[68]. However, hybridization is clearly occurring at a number of sites, particularly where sika stags are colonizing areas occupied predominantly by red deer or where red deer are colonizing areas previously occupied mainly by sika [67]. Once hybrids are present, experience from other areas shows that further hybridization can be rapid: in the southern Lake District of northwest England and the Wicklow Mountains in Ireland local hybridization has led to populations composed almost entirely of hybrids[68,76,77]. Mating can probably occur both between male sika and female red deer and between male red deer and female sika[67,76,77,78].

7.7 IMPLICATIONS FOR MANAGEMENT

The rapid growth and superior reproductive performance of forest-living red deer clearly demonstrates the potential effects of habitat improvement on red deer populations in the Highlands. However, where the density of forest-living populations approaches ecological carrying capacity, their reproductive performance may decline to levels similar to those on the open hill though they usually appear to show more rapid growth and larger body size[4,10].

Damage to trees by deer populations living in woodland and forestry poses a variety of management problems. In the long term, the most efficient way of protecting plantations from deer is likely to be the imposition of intensive control programmes combined with design of plantations to facilitate shooting[15,79,80,81]. In at least some forests, the costs of control programmes are largely or even totally covered by the sale of hunting permits and venison. Where this is practical, the central question is how much economic loss is caused by browsing and bark stripping in the long term. Research at Glenbranter suggests that this may be less than was previously feared[7].

Apart from problems of protecting plantations from marauding or resident deer, the spread of forestry in the Highlands poses three potential problems to managers, though reliable information on all three is sparse. First, where plantations are fenced the temporary exclosure of deer from substantial areas of their habitat may have a local influence on their numbers, growth and reproductive

Plate 7.2 Heavily browsed Norway spruce. (Photograph: Brian Staines.)

performance though this may be offset by the increased availability of shelter in winter. As we describe in Chapter 4, no systematic attempt has yet been made to investigate these effects.

Second, where deer can move between plantations and the open hill, animals may spend much of the day in cover, only visiting the open hill at night. This may impede culling. In addition, some forest owners believe that stags born on the open hill commonly emigrate into forestry populations (where they are likely to be shot in the course of control programmes) while few animals migrate in the opposite direction and if so, local dispersal into forestry could have an important influence on the number of stags that can be culled each year from populations living on the open hill. However, as yet,

Plate 7.3 Sitka spruce, bark-stripped by red deer. (Photograph: Brian Staines.)

we know too little about the frequency of immigration and emigration from forestry plantations to tell whether or not this is the case.

Finally, the spread of sika deer populations in association with forestry may well face managers with a serious problem in the future. Though hybridization between red deer and sika is still rare, it appears to be increasing and the experience in other areas suggests, that as numbers of hybrids rise, the rate of hybridization may increase rapidly[67]. Sika make better use of cover than red deer and are more difficult to control[67] so that eradicating them or preventing their spread may be difficult. In the long term, it may even be that the prevention of extensive hybridization is incompatible with increasing afforestation[67] and that offshore islands like Rhum and Jura provide the best hope of conserving red deer. Meanwhile, it is clear that encouraging further colonization by sika is irresponsible and that there are advantages to eliminating them where this is practicable.

7.8 SUMMARY

7.1 In many parts of the Highlands, red deer have colonized forestry plantations. Population densities in forests cover the same range as on the open hill, varying with the type and age of the forest. Population density is typically low in mature forests and is highest at the thicket stage of forest development.

7.2 The weight of both hinds and stags is often greater than on the open hill and reproductive performance is improved: in some forests, the majority of animals conceive as yearlings and produce a calf each year throughout the rest of their lives.

7.3 Within the forest, red deer spend much of their time feeding in rides, along streams and in clearings. In summer, their diet consists largely of grasses, with smaller amounts of forbs, conifers and broad-leaved trees while, in winter, the proportion of heather in the diet increases.

7.4 Browsing and bark stripping by red deer can reduce the growth rate of some conifers, damaging the eventual timber. Methods of controlling the impact of deer populations on forestry include exclosure, intensive control and the protection of individual trees with chemical or mechanical agents. In sizeable forests, exclosure is rarely effective for long while the costs of protecting individual trees are unacceptably high.

7.5 In many parts of the Highlands, red deer living in forestry plantations share their habitat with roe deer and/or sika deer. There is little evidence of competition between species, possibly because few populations of either species have yet reached ecological carrying capacity. However, hybridization between red deer and sika is currently occurring at low levels and may be expected to increase in the future. In the long run, the danger of extensive hybridization between red deer and sika poses an important threat to the integrity of Highland red deer populations.

7.6 Afforestation poses several problems to the management of Highland red deer populations. Though access to forestry is likely to improve growth and reproductive performance, immigration into commercial forests may affect the potential yield of neighbouring populations and the ease with which deer can be culled. The local effects of afforestation on the density and distribution of red deer have yet to be examined.

REFERENCES

1. Locke, G. M. L. (1976). *The Place of Forestry in Scotland*. Forestry Commission Research and Development Paper, **113**. H.M.S.O., Edinburgh.

2. Ratcliffe, P.R. (1987). *The Management of Red Deer in the Commercial Forests of Scotland Related to Population Dynamics and Habitat Changes*. D. Phil. thesis, University of London.

3. Stewart, L.K. (1988). 'Deer in Scotland', In: *The Changing Scene*, Red Deer Commission, Inverness.

4. Ratcliffe, P. R. (1984). 'Population dynamics of red deer (*Cervus elaphus* L.) in Scottish commercial forests'. *Proc. Roy. Soc. Edinb.*, **82B**, 291–302.

5. Ratcliffe, P. R. (1984). 'Population density and reproduction in red deer in Scottish commercial forests'. *Acta Zool. Fenn.*, **172**, 191–192.

6. Jeffery, W. G. (1974). 'The Galloway (red) deer control scheme'. *Deer*, **3**, 226–230.

7. Staines, B. W. & Welch, D. (1984). 'Habitat selection and impact of red (*Cervus elaphus* L.) and roe (*Capreolus capreolus* L.) deer in a Sitka spruce plantation'. *Proc. Roy. Soc. Edinb.*, **82B**, 303–391.

8. Catt, D. C. & Staines, B. W. (1987). 'Home range use and habitat selection by red deer (*Cervus elaphus*) in a Sitka spruce plantation as determined by radio-tracking'. *J. Zool.*, **211**, 681–693.

9. Hinge, M. (1986). *Ecology of Red and Roe Deer in a Mixed-age Conifer Plantation: Comparative Studies on Habitat Selection, Ranging Behaviour and Feeding Strategies*. D.Phil. thesis, University of Aberdeen.

10. Mitchell, B., Grant, W. & Cubby, J. (1981). 'Notes on performance of red deer *Cervus elaphus* in a woodland habitat'. *J. Zool.*, **194**, 279–284.

11. Mitchell, B. & McCowan, D. (1980). 'Estimating and comparing population densities of red deer *Cervus elaphus* L. in concealing habitats'. Institute of Terrestrial Ecology Annual Report, Institute of Terrestrial Ecology, Cambridge.

12. Ratcliffe, P.R. (1987). 'Red deer population changes in woodland and the independent assessment of population size'. In: *Mammal Population Studies*, ed. S. Harris. Smyp. Zoological Society, Lond., **58**, 153–165.

13. Staines, B.W. & Ratcliffe, P.R. (1987). 'Establishing the abundance of red deer (*Cervus elaphus* L.) and roe deer (*Capreolus capreolus* L.) and their current status'. *Symp. Zool. Soc. Lond.*, **58**, 131–152.

14. Ratcliffe, P. R. & Petty, S. J. (1987). 'The management of commercial forests for wildlife'. In: *Trees and Wildife in the Scottish*

Uplands, ed. D. Jenkins, pp. 177–187. Institute of Terrestrial Ecology, Huntingdon.

15. Ratcliffe, P.R., Hall, J. & Allan, J. (1986). 'Computer predictions of sequential growth changes in commercial forests as an aid to wildlife management, with reference to red deer'. *Scottish Forestry,* **40**, 79–83.

16. Mitchell, B., Staines, B. W. & Welch, D. (1977). *Ecology of Red Deer, a Research Review Relevant to their Management in Scotland.* Institute of Terrestrial Ecology, Cambridge.

17. Clutton-Brock, T. H., Guinness, F. E. & Albon, S. D. (1982). *Red Deer: the Behavior and Ecology of Two Sexes.* University of Chicago Press, Chicago.

18. Petrie, S. M. (1951). *History of Glenbranter Forest, 1921–1951.* Mimeographed report, Forestry Commission.

19. Staines, B. W., Welch, D., Catt, D. C., Scott, D. & Hinge, M. D. C. (1985). 'Habitat use and feeding by deer in Sitka spruce plantations'. *Institute of Terrestrial Ecology Annual Report 1984*, 12–16. Natural Environment Research Council, Swindon.

20. Thirgood, S. J. (1984). *The Effect of Distance from Cover Upon the Utilization of Restocked Sitka Spruce (Picea sitchensis L.) Plantations by Red Deer (Cervus elaphus L.) and Roe Deer (Capreolus capreolus L.).* Honours thesis, University of Aberdeen.

21. Ahlen, I. (1965). 'Studies on the red deer, *Cervus elaphus* L. in 'Scandinavia III – Ecological Investigations'. Viltrevy **3**, 177–376.

22. Douglas, M. J. W. (1971). 'Behaviour responses of red deer and chamois to cessation of hunting'. *New Z. J. of Sci.,* **14**, 507–518.

23. Holloway, C. W. (1968). 'The protection of man-made forests from wildlife'. In: *World Symposium on Man-made Forests and their Industrial Importance,* 687–715, F.A.O., Rome.

24. Vanek, J. (1956). 'Regeneration of young forest trees damaged by deer'. *Lesn. Pr.,* **35**, 314–319.

25. Holloway, C. W. (1967). *The Effect of Red Deer and Other Animals on Naturally Regenerated Scots Pine.* Ph.D. thesis, University of Aberdeen.

26. Eiberle, K. (1975). 'Results of a simulation of game damage by cutting the shoots'. *Schweiz. Z. Forstwes.,* **126**, 821–839.

27. Sablina, T. B. (1959). 'Adaptive peculiarities of the feeding of certain species of ungulates and the influence of these species on changes in the vegetation'. *Soobshch. Inst. Lesa,* **13**, 32–43.

28. Dzieciolowski, R. (1970). 'Food selectivity in the red deer towards twigs of trees, shrubs and dwarf shrubs'. *Acta theriol.,* **15**, 361–365.

29. Bobek, B., Weiner, J. & Zielinski, J. (1972). 'Food supply and its consumption by deer in a deciduous forest of southern Poland'. *Acta theriol.,* **17**, 187–202.

30. Ueckermann, E. (1960). *Wildstandsbewirtschaftung und Wildschaden-*

verhutung beim Rotwild. Paul Parey, Berlin and Hamburg.
31. Chard, J. S. R. (1966). 'The red deer of Furness Fells'. *Forestry,* **39**, 135–150.
32. Badenoch, C. O. (1971). 'Survey of damage by deer in plantation woodland'. In: *Range Ecology Research*, 1st Progress Report 45–46. Nature Conservancy, Edinburgh.
33. Stickles, A. (1971). *A Study of Red Deer Damage and the Costs of Fence Protection*. Honours thesis, University of Edinburgh.
34. Stubbe, C. (1970). 'Barking damage by red deer in forestry – causes, effects and prevention'. *Wiss. Z. Tech. Hochsch. Univ. Dresden*, **19**, 171–178.
35. Reijnders, P. J. H. & Veen, H. E. van de (1974). 'On the causes of bark stripping by red deer and on the relation between management of red deer and forestry in the Dutch setting'. *Ned. Boschb Tijdschr.*, **46**, 113–138.
36. Stenin, G. (1970). 'Feeding of red deer in winter and its effect in reducing damage'. *Gorsko Stop.*, **26**, 40–44.
37. Muller, H. J. (1965). 'Investigations regarding the evaluation of the economically acceptable density of game peeling in forests according to the damage caused by game to the site'. *Arch. Forstw.*, **14**, 533–561.
38. Ueckermann, E. (1956). 'Studies on the cause of debarking by red deer'. *Z. Jagdwiss.*, **2**, 123–131.
39. Strandgaard, H. (1967). 'A study of the relationship of red deer to the modern cultivated landscape of Denmark'. *Dansk. Viltunders*, **13**, 9–75.
40. McIntyre, E. B. (1972). 'Bark-stripping – a natural phenomenon'. *Scott. For.*, **26**, 43–50.
41. Pellew, R. A. (1968). *Bark-Stripping: a Problem in the Integrated Management of Red Deer and Forestry*. Honours thesis, University of Edinburgh.
42. Rijcken, P. H. P. (1965). 'Debarking of Scots pine by red deer'. *Ned. Boschb Tijdschr.*, **37**, 30–64.
43. Szederjei, A. (1957). 'Bark peeling by red deer'. *Z. Jagdwiss.*, **3**, 101–107.
44. Krugge, W. (1975). 'The effect of peeling damage caused by red deer on wood quality of Norway spruce and beech'. *Forstarchiv.*, **46**, 32–38.
45. Maxwell, H. A. (1967). 'Red deer and forestry with special reference to the Highlands of Scotland'. *Deer*, **1**, 126–130.
46. Nannestad, L. (1970). 'The effect of barking by red deer on the economy of Norway spruce'. *Hedeselsk. Tidsskr. Aarhaus.*, **91**, 5–22.
47. Zaruba, C. & Snadjr, J. (1966). 'The effect of bark stripping by red deer on timber volume production'. *Lesn. Cas.*, **12**, 81–100.

48. Kurth, A. (1964). 'Assessment of deer damage in Canton Schwyz'. *Schweiz. Z. Forstwes.*, **115**, 1–12.
49. Habeck, J. R. (1960). 'Winter deer activity in the white cedar swamps of northern Wisconsin'. *Ecology*, **41**, 327–333.
50. McNeil, R. J. (1964). 'Interactions between man, deer and vegetation in Michigan'. *Proc. N.Z. Ecol. Soc.*, **11**, 44–48.
51. Houston, D. B. (1982). *The Northern Yellowstone Elk, Ecology and Management*. Macmillan, New York.
52. Vrublovski, K. I. (1912). 'The theoretical differentiation between browsing and grazing ruminants and its practical significance'. *Arkh. vet. Nauk.*, **8**, 746–778,
53. Westhoff, V. (1967). 'The impact of game stock on vegetation'. *Ned. Boschb Tijdschr.*, **39**, 218–232.
54. Steven, H. M. & Carlisle, A. (1959). *The Native Pinewoods of Scotland*. Oliver and Boyd, London.
55. Ehrlich, H. (1963). 'Winter enclosures as a means of reducing barking damage by red deer'. *Allg. Forstztg.*, **74**, 119–123.
56. Jenkins, D. & Reuss, Prinz H. III (1969). 'A successful case-history reconciling forestry and red deer management'. *Forestry*, **42**, 21–27.
57. Paslawski, T. (1970). 'Protection of pine plantations against browsing by cervids'. *Proc. Int. Congr. Game Biol.*, **9**, 773–775.
58. Pepper, A. W. (1978). 'Chemical repellents'. *Forestry Commission Leaflet*, **73**, H.M.S.O., London.
59. Fanta, B. (1966). 'Bark scraping: a method of protecting Norway spruce from deer damage'. *Lesn. Pr.*, **45**, 258–260.
60. Nahlik, A. J. de. (1958) *Wild Deer*, Faber and Faber, London.
61. Haaften, J. L. van (1965). 'A natural repellent'. *Proc. Int. Congr. Game Biol.*, **6**, 389–392.
62. König, E. (1970). 'Effects of fresh food on the prevention of peeling damage by red deer'. *Proc. Int. Congr. Game Biol.*, **9**, 176–181.
63. Bubenik, A. B. & Lochman, J. (1956). 'Futterverbrauch und Tagesrhythmus der Futteraufnahme beim Reh- und Rotwild'. *Z. Jagdwiss.*, **2**, 112–118.
64. Veen, H. E. van de (1973). 'Bark stripping of coniferous trees by red deer'. *Deer*, **3**, 15–21.
65. Loudon, A. S. I. (1979). *Social Behaviour and Habitat in Roe Deer (Capreolus capreolus)*. Ph.D. thesis, University of Edinburgh.
66. Batchelor, C. L. (1960). 'A study of the relations between roe and fallow deer with special reference to Drummond Hill Forest, Scotland'. *J. Anim. Ecol.*, **29**, 375–384.
67. Ratcliffe, P. R. (1987). 'Distribution and current status of sika deer, *Cervus nippon*, in Great Britain'. *Mammal Review*, **17**, 39–58.
68. Lowe, V. P. W. & Gardiner, A. S. (1975). 'Hybridization between red deer (*Cervus elaphus*) and sika deer (*Cervus nippon*) with particular

reference to stocks in N.W. England'. *J. Zool.*, **177**, 553–566.

69. Lowe, V. P. W. (1979). *Wild and Feral Deer in Great Britain*. Unpublished report, Natural Environment Research Council, Swindon.
70. Schubeler, W. (1984). 'Sika deer in Europe; Weserbergland'. *Deer*, **6**, 76–77.
71. Eick, E. (1984). 'Sika deer in Europe; Mohnesee'. *Deer*, **6**, 76.
72. Mann, J. C. E. (1982). *The Social Organisation and Ecology of the Japanese Sika Deer (Cervus nippon) in Southern England*. Ph.D. thesis, University of Southampton.
73. Hofmann, R. R. (1982). 'Morphological classification of sika deer within the comparative system of ruminant feeding types'. *Deer*, **5**, 352–353.
74. Logan, P. C. (1957). 'The Japanese deer herd; spread, density and control problems'. *New Zealand Forestry Service Report*, SF90/1.
75. Kiddie, D. G. (1962). 'The sika deer in New Zealand'. *New Zealand Forestry Information Series*, **44**, 1–35.
76. Harrington, R. (1973). 'Hybridization among deer and its implications for conservation'. *Irish Forest. J.*, **30**, 64–78.
77. Harrington, R. (1982). 'The hybridization of red deer (*Cervus elaphus* L. 1758) and Japanese sika deer (*C. nippon* Temminck 1838)'. *Transaction of the International Congress of Game Biology*, **14**, 559–571.
78. Harrington, R. (1974). 'The hybridization of red and sika deer in Northern Ireland'. *Irish Forest. J.*, **31**, 2–3.
79. Ratcliffe, P. R. & Rowe, J. J. (1985). 'A biological basis for managing red and roe deer in British commercial forests'. *XVII Int. Congr. Game Biol.* 17–21, Brussels.
80. Ratcliffe, P.R. (1987). 'The management of red deer in upland forests'. *Forestry Commission Bulletin*, **71** H.M.S.O., London.
81. Ratcliffe, P.R. (1985). 'Glades for deer control in upland forests'. *Forestry Commission Leaflet*, **86** H.M.S.O., London.

8 Red Deer Research and Management

8.1 INTRODUCTION

In this final chapter, we briefly synthesize what is known of the population dynamics of Highland red deer (Section 8.2) and discuss the relevance of research to management decisions concerning stocking density, culling rates and regimes (Section 8.3). In Section 8.4, we consider the two main decisions facing Highland deer managers: what management objectives to adopt and how many deer to maintain? There are large gaps in our knowledge both of natural ecological processes and of the effects of management on deer populations. Moreover, variation in estate size and habitat quality preclude specific recommendations on management that will be suitable for all areas. Nonetheless, research on the ecology of Highland red deer provides a framework for predicting the likely consequences of different management practices which should help deer managers to adapt general principles to the needs of particular populations.

8.2 POPULATION DYNAMICS OF RED DEER IN THE HIGHLANDS

The density of red deer on open ground in the Highlands ranges from less than five animals per square kilometre to over 20 animals per square kilometre (Figure 2.5). Outside forestry and woodland, red deer are most abundant in areas where high ground, subalpine soils and peaty podzols are common and where the density of sheep and the rate of culling are relatively low (Figure 2.8). Average density has changed substantially since 1960, falling to less than 8 deer per square kilometre in the late 1960s before rising to around 11 or 12 deer per square kilometre in the late 1970s and early 1980s (Figure 2.2). The rise of deer numbers between 1967 and 1975 was associated with milder winters, drier, warmer summers and a reduction in the number of hill sheep in the Highlands (Figure 2.3).

As a result of detailed studies of particular deer populations, notably on Rhum and at Glenfeshie, we have a detailed understanding of the consequences of changes in population density. As in many other mammals[1], high density is associated with later ages at first breeding, reduced growth, lower fecundity and rising juvenile mortality in winter and these changes gradually reduce the rate of population growth (Chapter 5). Lower fecundity at high density is probably caused partly by a reduction in the weight and condition of hinds and partly by an increase in the weight at which females are likely to conceive[2,3]. As in reindeer, changes in juvenile mortality are caused partly by later dates of conception and birth[2,4], which reduce the period available for growth before the onset of winter. In addition, at high population density, birth weight exerts a stronger effect on survival and light-born calves are progressively less likely to survive[4].

The form of density-dependent changes evidently varies between different aspects of growth and reproductive performance. On Rhum, while some parameters changed most rapidly during the later stages of population growth, others showed an approximately linear rate of change or even changed most rapidly in the early stages of population growth (see Figure 5.10). One factor that may have strengthened the effects of changes in population density in the initial stages of population growth was the relationship between group size and reproductive success. As population size increased, some matrilineal groups grew faster than others. In larger groups, fecundity was reduced and calf mortality was relatively high[6,7] though these effects disappeared at high population density[8], possibly because the effects of competition between groups masked those of competition within them. Similar effects of group size on reproduction in mammals occur in a wide variety of other social species where daughters join their mothers' social groups[6]. Since an early response to rising density contributes to population stability, whereas delayed density-dependent responses can cause population instability[9], animals living in closed matrilineal groups may be less likely to show dramatic changes in population size than species where female dispersal is common.

Other aspects of reproduction appear to be less strongly affected by increasing numbers. Neither birth weight nor neonatal survival changed consistently as population density increased in the North Block of Rhum (Chapter 5) and the relationship between density and adult mortality was weak (see Chapter 5). In addition, rising population density on Rhum was not associated with increased rates of (permanent) dispersal in either sex. Hinds, in particular, usually adopted home ranges overlapping those of their mother and were reluctant to change them, even where local density was high and reproductive performance depressed. Studies of a variety of other mammals show that adult mortality is usually less sensitive to changes in food availability than fecundity and juvenile mortality[1] while recent work on other species where females live in matrilineal groups also shows that individuals seldom disperse, even when local population density reaches a level at which reproductive performance is depressed[6].

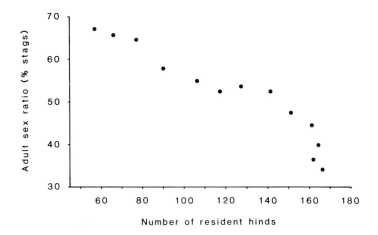

Figure 8.1 Changes in the adult sex ratio (% stags) in the North Block of Rhum as population density increased between 1971 and 1983.

Variation in climate, too, can have an important influence on growth, recruitment and survival. On Rhum, high rainfall in autumn is associated with high calf mortality in winter and low fecundity the following June. In contrast, in the drier, colder climate of the central and eastern Highlands, the duration of snow cover in winter is more closely related to reproductive performance and survival than autumn rainfall (see Table 6.1). Variation in spring weather on Rhum causes pronounced differences in the reproductive performance of successive cohorts of females that persist through-out the animal's lifespan (see Section 6.9). Low average temperatures in April and May are associated with a reduction in birth weight. Cohorts of hinds born in cold springs show low fecundity throughout the rest of their lives and their calves are born at below average weight and show high mortality (see Section 6.9).

It is clear that both high population density and adverse weather can affect males and females to different extents. As numbers increased in our study area, the mortality of juvenile males rose more rapidly than the mortality of juvenile females (Figure 5.7), contributing to an increased bias towards hinds in the adult sex ratio (Figure 8.1). Antler size in yearling and adult males declined rapidly as population density rose (Chapter 5). The large increase in male body size in populations of red deer living in forestry (see Figure 7.1) suggests that the common tendency for food shortage to affect the

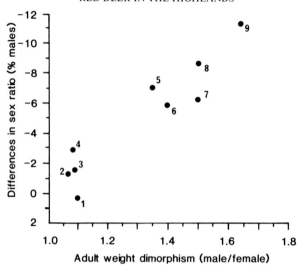

Figure 8.2   Differences in the sex ratio (% males) between birth and the end of the first year of life in free-ranging populations of ungulates, showing different degrees of adult weight dimorphism ($\bar{x}$ male weight/$\bar{x}$ female weight). 1, Zebra; 2, sable; 3, roe deer; 4, feral horse; 5, Soay sheep; 6, wapiti; 7, red deer; 8, black- tailed deer; 9, reindeer.[10]

growth of males more than that of females[10] also occurs in red deer. One likely explanation of the greater susceptibility of males to food deprivation is that their energetic requirements exceed those of females because of their larger size, for in vertebrates where males and females are of similar size, sex differences in juvenile growth and mortality are usually small (see Figure 8.2).

Rising hind numbers in the North Block of Rhum were associated with increased segregation between the sexes and a reduction in the extent to which stags used areas of short greens strongly preferred by hinds (Chapter 4). One explanation of this trend is that, because of their larger body size, stags have greater energetic requirements than hinds. However, the rate at which they can ingest food may not be much higher than that of hinds since it may be governed by the breadth of their incisor arcade. Stags may consequently require greater food availability than hinds in order to cover their daily energy requirements and may avoid areas strongly preferred by hinds, including swards dominated by herbs and narrow-leaved grasses, where food availability has been reduced to low levels[11-13]. Feeding competition with hinds may exclude stags from the most heavily used swards and this may contribute to the decline in stag numbers in areas where hind density is high. The alternative strategy of actively defending feeding sites against hinds may not be open to them because food resources are widely dispersed.

There are many substantial gaps in our understanding of the natural dynamics of Highland red deer populations. In particular, four questions of fundamental importance have still to be answered. To our knowledge, none of them have yet been satisfactorily answered for any other population of wild ungulates.

Are density-dependent changes in recruitment and survival caused by changes in total population density or by the density of females alone? Similarly, are density-dependent changes in the growth and antler size of stags caused by variation in total density, hind density or stag density?

Since hinds and followers compete for food primarily with each other, we suspect that reduced fecundity and increased juvenile mortality at high population density are a response to changes in hind numbers rather than to the combined density of hinds and stags. Moreover, while antler growth in the North Block of Rhum was negatively related to hind density (see Figure 5.11), it was *positively* related to stag density, which declined as hind numbers rose. As we argue in Chapter 4, this suggests that competition with hinds may be partly responsible for changes in the performance and survival of stags. In some other mammals, too, there is evidence that the density of females alone is the primary determinant of recruitment and survival[14-16].

How does the density of hinds affect the rate of immigration and emigration by stags?

Little is known of dispersal in Highland red deer, except on Rhum where it may be partly constricted by the size of the island (see Chapter 3). The Red Deer Commission's tagging programmes show that stags are shot further from their place of birth than hinds but do not tell us whether this is the result of permanent emigration of two- to four-year-olds or of temporary emigration of mature animals in the rut.

The available information from other red deer populations[17-19], as well as the prevalence of male dispersal in mammals[20] suggests that a substantial proportion of young stags probably emigrate from their natal area. Consequently, local rates of immigration and emigration may have a substantial effect on the number of stags resident on particular deer forests. The factors affecting immigration and emigration rates of males in Highland red deer are unknown but may include the population density of hinds (see Chapter 5).

Where population density is limited by food quality and availability, at what time of year are resources limiting?

The most likely answer appears to be that food quality and availability in winter limits population size but that this is affected by production during the summer months. In particular, we suspect that food availability at the beginning and end of winter has an important influence on mortality because it determines the duration of the period of winter starvation. However, food availability at different times of year is inter-correlated and it is consequently difficult to determine when supplies are limiting. Experimental manipulation of food availability at different times of year will be necessary to pinpoint the precise time at which resources limit population density. In this context it is interesting that, on Rhum, fertilisation of coastal swards by nesting gulls, which primarily affects the quality of forage in summer, has a substantial influence on local population density as well as on reproductive performance[21].

What factors determine the degree of stability or instability that unculled deer populations show?

In the past, it was commonly feared that, in the absence of predators, unculled deer populations would rapidly increase, then crash, and this concern was one of the reasons for the formation of the Red Deer Commission itself[22]. Today, it is clear that the absence of control by culling or by natural predators does not necessarily lead to large-scale population instability and that ungulate populations can be limited by resource availability even where predators are present[9,23-27]. The degree of stability found in unculled populations of ungulates varies widely. When ungulates have been introduced to unoccupied habitats where food is abundant, their numbers usually increase rapidly. In some cases, this is succeeded by a gradual reduction of population growth as density-dependent factors reduce the rate of recruitment, followed by stabilization at a density where the population is in equilibrium with its food supply[27,28]. In other cases, a rapid initial increase in numbers is followed by a rapid decline and then by stabilization at a density often substantially below that achieved at the peak[29]. And in a few, oscillations in population size continue[30], sometimes leading to population extinction[31]. The size of the initial oscillation and the degree of stability that succeeds it depend on the dynamic relationship between herbivores and their food supply[9,32,33]. Strong density-dependence in herbivore recruitment or survival and resistance to over-grazing in the plant populations they feed on encourages stability while weak density-dependence associated with a food supply that is sensitive to over-grazing can lead to instability or even to the local extinction of the herbivore. Several of the best documented examples of irruptions followed by over-grazing and extinction are of reindeer populations introduced to offshore islands in the Arctic where they initially exploited and then over-grazed lichens[27,31]. However, where reindeer are introduced to Arctic or Antarctic habitats where they feed principally on vascular plants, less sensitive to over-grazing, populations usually stabilize and extinctions are rare[27].

In the absence of human interference, it appears that populations of red deer and elk rarely show the drastic crashes observed in some populations of reindeer and sheep[34–36]. There may be at least two reasons for this. First, as Chapter 5 describes, the rate of recruitment is closely related to population density, partly because of the structure of female groups. Second, many of their food plants are relatively resistant to grazing (see Chapter 4) and, where these are not (as in the case of aspen and willow), the rate of decline is usually too slow to cause a sudden reduction in population size. This is not to say that Highland deer populations will not respond to climatic changes. As we describe in Chapter 6, harsh weather in autumn and winter can increase mortality of juveniles and adults, reducing population size[37,38].

Another important source of instability in unculled populations may be the effects of climate on early development and reproductive performance that we describe in Section 6.9. If good and bad springs occur at random, they will sometimes occur in runs, generating

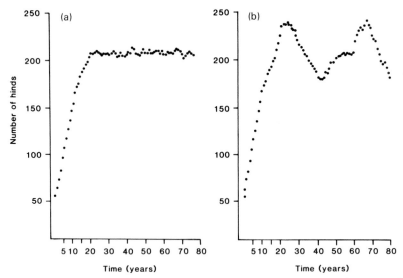

Figure 8.3 A simple model of the predicted growth of the population in the North Block of Rhum based on (a) density-dependent age-specific fertility and survival including random variation in the birth sex ratio using data for 1971 to 1985 and (b) the same relationships used in (a) together with differences in cohort quality (using cohorts born between 1968 and 1979) added randomly as good, average or poor.

several 'good' or 'bad' cohorts in succession. As these cohorts pass through the population, they are likely to cause changes in recruitment and in population size. In Figure 8.3, we have modelled the effects of a random distribution of cohort quality within the range of cohorts observed on Rhum between 1968 and 1979 on variation in hind numbers. As the figure shows, the effects of randomly generated runs of good and bad cohorts may be substantial compared to a simple density-dependent model, though they are likely to be eroded by culling (see below).

8.3   MANAGEMENT AND POPULATION DYNAMICS

Less is known about the effects of management on Highland red deer populations than about the natural processes of population dynamics. Management practices that are likely to be important include the numbers of sheep and cattle maintained on the hill (see Sections 2.2 and 2.3), the frequency with which hill vegetation is burned (Section 4.6), draining, fertilisation or reseeding of low ground, supplementary feeding (Section 4.7) and afforestation

(Chapter 7). High sheep densities may depress deer numbers and performance (see Section 4.8), while muirburn and habitat improvement are likely to increase them (Section 4.6). Access to forestry plantations provides shelter during the winter and access to novel food supplies and is associated with a substantial improvement in reproductive performance and growth, especially in stags (see Chapter 7) but where deer are fenced out of plantations (as in many areas of west and northern Scotland), afforestation may depress population density and performance. However, the magnitude of these effects is not yet known.

The management practice that most directly affects Highland deer populations is culling policy for, in most parts of the Highlands, between 6 and 12% of hinds counted in spring and between 10 and 17% of stags are killed each year (see Figure 2.10). So far, little attempt has been made to investigate the effects of culling practices on Highland deer populations[but see 39-41]. Four important questions need to be answered:

(1) What rate of culling is necessary to control population size and how can this be calculated?

An average cull of one-sixth of the adult population in spring is widely recommended, based on an average ratio of 33 calves to 100 hinds in spring (see Chapter 2). However, there are two fundamental objections to any proposal to apply a standard culling rate to all Highland red deer populations. First, the number of animals that must be taken to stabilize population size will depend on the proximity of the population to ecological carrying capacity[41,42]. Populations close to ecological carrying capacity, where fecundity and juvenile survival are low, will require smaller culls to stabilize density than those that are substantially below carrying capacity and show high fecundity and survival. Second, differences in habitat quality throughout the Highlands are substantial and presumably contribute to differences in calf/hind ratios which range from 25 calves per hundred hinds at the lower extreme to 50 per hundred at the top (see Appendix 5). Assuming a 50:50 sex ratio in recruits and adult mortality of around 3% per year, the maximum percentage of the adult population in spring that can be culled each year without reducing population size the following season may vary between areas from less than 10% to over 20%.

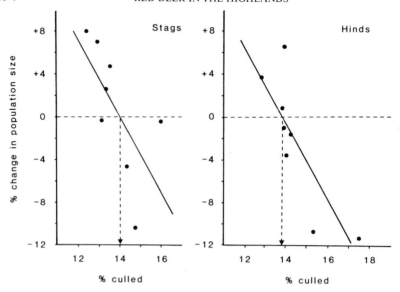

Figure 8.4   Changes in the population size of stags and hinds ⩾1 year old on Rhum, 1958–1965, in years following culls of different sizes.

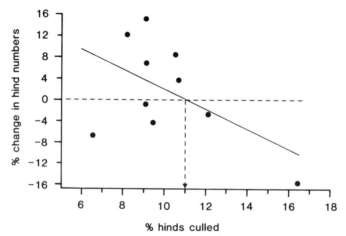

Figure 8.5   Changes in population size of hinds ⩾1 year old outside the North Block of Rhum, 1977–1986, in years following culls of different sizes.

Unless culling rates are adjusted to variation in recruitment and mortality, they are likely either to fail to control deer numbers or to reduce them. In theory, the solution is to adjust culling levels to local variation in recruitment but, in practice, the latter is seldom easy to estimate accurately (see Appendix 1). Because of this problem, we believe that the most practical approach to determining cull size is to manipulate the numbers of animals culled while monitoring the effects on deer numbers by repeated local counts[43]. For example, in Figure 8.4 we have plotted the proportion of stags and hinds counted in spring which were culled the same year on Rhum against the percentage change in the size of the island's population. This shows that, between 1958 and 1965, an annual cull of 14% maintained the numbers of both sexes at a constant level. Culling above this rate was associated with a decline in numbers while culling below it allowed numbers to rise. Where the aim is to maximize the sustainable yield that can be taken from a population rather than to stabilize numbers, the same approach can be taken in order to identify the deer density at which the largest cull can be taken (see Chapter 5).

Changes in climate that affect recruitment or mortality will also be likely to affect the culling rate needed to maintain density at a stable level. For example, when we repeated the analysis described above for hinds on Rhum for the period 1977 to 1986, when wet autumns and cold winters reduced the number of animals recruited each year, the population could, on average, sustain no more than an 11% annual cull without declining (see Figure 8.5).

An additional advantage of this approach to identifying the rate of culling necessary to control numbers is that it is less likely to be affected by biases in counting deer than most other methods of deciding culling rate. Attempts to calculate culling rates using estimates of recruitment will obviously be affected by errors in counting or classification. For example, if the number of stags on Rhum is consistently underestimated in annual counts and the number of hinds is overestimated (as some reconstructions suggest: see Appendix 1), an annual cull of 14% of the *actual* stag population between 1958 and 1965 might have been excessive while a 14% cull of the *actual* number of hinds might not have been sufficient to control numbers. However, so long as counting biases are consistent, this is unimportant for practical purposes for, as Figure 8.4 demonstrates, an annual cull of 14% of the *perceived* population was sufficient to control the numbers of both sexes.

(2) How does variation in culling rates affect population density?

Where culling rates approach the level of recruitment, it is obvious that culling may hold population density below the level to which it would rise if culls were ceased. The population of the North Block

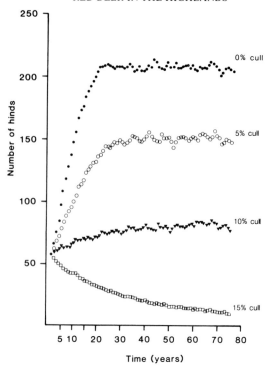

Figure 8.6 Models of the likely effects of four different culling regimes on a population of red deer hinds. The basic model incorporating density-dependent changes in recruitment and survival but no cull (0%) is the same as in Figure 8.3(a). Imposing a 5% cull reduces the population at equilibrium from 210 to 150. Raising the cull to 10% allows the population to grow slowly to approximately 80 hinds. A 15% cull is not sustainable and the population declines.

of Rhum provides a good example of the effects of culling on red deer populations. Prior to 1970, around 14% of hinds and 12% of stags resident in the block were culled each year. Cessation of the cull in 1972 was followed by an increase in hind numbers, which rose by 200% by 1983 and are still rising (see Figure 5.1). Stag numbers initially rose and then declined after 1978. Whether or not similar changes in population density would occur in other red deer populations released from culls close to the level of recruitment would depend on the stage of population growth at which the cull was originally imposed.

However, in many areas of the Highlands, hind culls are probably lower than the level of recruitment and have been so for many years (see Chapter 2). What effect is variation in culling rate likely to have in these areas? Even where they are substantially lower than the level of recruitment, culling rates may have an important influence on the size of populations at equilibrium[9,32,33,42]. In Figure 8.6 we have modelled the likely effects of culling 5%, 10% and 15% of the hinds in our study area on Rhum. The age distribution of the 'culls' incorporated in the model followed the age distribution of culls taken from the rest of Rhum. The initial model incorporated changes in age structure and density dependence in recruitment and survival but assumed that selective culling did not reduce natural mortality in each age class. As Figure 8.6 shows, culls substantially below the level of recruitment can still have an important effect on population size. The introduction of variation in cohort quality does not alter this conclusion.

However, if instead of assuming that culling did not affect mortality at each age, we had assumed that all animals culled would otherwise have died or dispersed from the population, we would have reached quite a different conclusion. In this case, culling would have had no effect on the eventual size of the equilibrium population. Both assumptions are unrealistic, but they highlight the importance of the third question that needs to be answered.

(3) How does culling affect natural mortality?

The answer to this question is likely to be affected both by the rate of culling and by the degree of selectivity across and within age classes. In most populations, the real relationship between culling and natural mortality presumably lies somewhere between the two extremes outlined above. Unfortunately, little is known of the effects of culling in red deer or in other deer species since natural mortality is usually difficult to monitor accurately.

Evidence from Rhum suggests that culling and the associated reduction in population density has an important influence on natural mortality in years when weather conditions are unfavourable. After the Nature Conservancy took possession of Rhum in 1957, the annual cull was raised from 6% to 17% of the numbers counted in spring. Lowe[44,45] suggests that this was responsible for a 75% reduction in natural mortality, which fell from 15.9% in stags and 17.6% in hinds in 1957 to 3.2% and 3.5% respectively in 1959. However, this comparison was based on two selected years and the original mortality levels observed in 1957 were substantially higher than the average level of winter mortality observed in the (unculled)

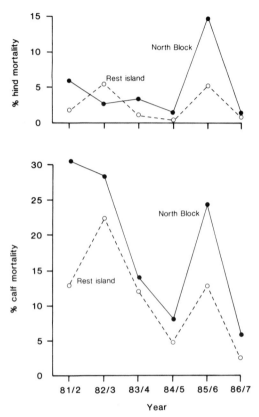

Figure 8.7 Mortality in the unculled North Block of Rhum 1981–1987 compared to the rest of the island. Mortality is calculated as the number of animals found dead by the island stalkers divided by the number found dead plus the number counted in the spring count.

North Block between 1972 and 1987 (see below). Comparisons of natural mortality between 1981 and 1986 in the (unculled) North Block compared to the rest of the island show that differences in mortality were often slight but were substantial in poor years (Figure 8.7). Smaller differences in culling rate may have little effect on natural mortality. For example, between 1958 and 1965 there was no consistent correlation between the size of the annual cull on Rhum and mortality in winter (Figure 8.8).

Across populations, the extent to which culling reduces natural mortality is likely to depend on the strength of density-independent factors affecting survival. In populations where bad weather causes substantial density-independent mortality across all age classes, the effects of culling on natural mortality are likely to be relatively weak

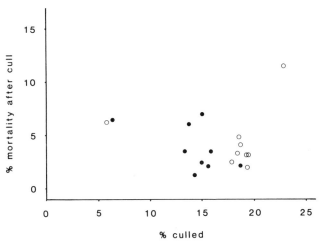

Figure 8.8 Annual (percentage) mortality of stags (●) and hinds (o) in the year following culls of different sizes on Rhum, 1958–1965 [44].

and population density at equilibrium will be strongly affected by differences in culling rate. Conversely, where natural mortality is closely related to population density, culling may have a stronger influence on natural mortality and the effects of variation in culling rates on population density may be reduced.

(4) How does selective culling affect reproductive performance and growth?

Though the importance of selective culling is regularly stressed, little is known of its effects. Claims that selection of stags with poor heads improves the quality of heads produced by subsequent generations have yet to be supported by systematic evidence. Though selection presumably has some effect, we would not be surprised if many decades of selective culling were necessary to produce a measurable change in the quality of heads.

The advantages of selectively culling old hinds are also regularly discussed[39,40]. We are again sceptical that this is likely to have a major effect on reproductive performance or survival, for in most parts of the Highlands, it is not easy to be consistently selective. Moreover, as we describe in Chapter 3, a hind's chances of surviving the winter and of breeding successfully the following year do not appear to deteriorate until she is over thirteen years old. In a culled population, only a small proportion of animals will reach this age. In contrast, selection for animals with poor calves may help to eliminate poor breeders from the population and may reduce calf mortality in winter.

8.4 MANAGEMENT DECISIONS

The management of Highland red deer populations requires two main decisions: what objectives should management aim at? and what population density should be maintained? No simple answer can be given to either question for both depend on the manager's priorities.

Consider the contrasting viewpoints of five different managers of Highland red deer populations. The first, who manages a nature reserve, is primarily interested in fostering the natural regeneration of native woodlands or, at least, with preventing their further deterioration. He will probably favour very low densities of red deer, or he may wish to eliminate deer altogether, for only the very lowest levels of red deer density are compatible with natural regeneration of woodlands in many parts of the Highlands today (see Chapter 7). He may also take a similar view of sheep and minimize their numbers as well.

The second manager, a sheep farmer, may also favour very low deer densities to minimize feeding competition with his flocks. He will not have a strong scientific basis for his decision, for we currently know virtually nothing about the effects of deer density on the numbers or reproductive performance of sheep, but his decision may be the right one for all that.

The third deer manager is primarily interested in the number of mature stags that he can shoot each year and in the size of their antlers. His decision is not straightforward for the number of stags he can kill is likely to be affected by the number that temporarily immigrate on to his ground during the rut as well as by the rate of permanent immigration and emigration by young stags, and little is known about the effects of local population density on these processes (see Section 5.5). However, assuming that his land holds a resident population of stags throughout the year, he may favour a relatively low density of hinds, for this is likely to increase the food available to stags, allowing young stags to grow rapidly and mature animals to produce large antlers. He would probably be well advised to instigate a relatively heavy hind cull and to keep sheep densities as low as is economically feasible. Though the absolute density of hinds that he should maintain will be affected by the quality of his ground, he should probably ensure that hinds do not substantially outnumber stags, even though this is likely to reduce the total number of animals of all sexes that he can extract from the population each year. The provision of shelter, access to forestry plantations, improvement of spring grazing and winter feeding may all help him to achieve his goal.

The fourth manager is primarily interested in the quantity of venison he can extract from the hill rather than in the size of individual beasts. To maximize venison offtake, he will prefer a higher density of hinds than that favoured by the previous manager. Maximum yield is usually achieved at a population density high enough to depress the growth of individual animals (see Section 5.6). He may also have to tolerate higher mortality of calves in winter and an adult sex ratio biased towards hinds to achieve his objective (see Chapter 5).

The last manager, like the first, runs a nature reserve but he either has no woodland to protect or his woodlands are safely fenced and he is primarily interested in maintaining the diversity of plants and animals. If red deer are the dominant herbivores, he may favour a high population density to provide sufficient grazing pressure to maintain species diversity in grassland and hinder the spread of *Molinia* into other communities (see Section 4.5). Indeed, he may decide to cease culling altogether and to allow the population to find a natural equilibrium. This will have the advantage that he is able to minimize expenditure on deer management though he may be un-popular with his neighbours if his reserve borders areas of farmland or forestry. He will also have to tolerate reduced growth and fecundity in his deer population, a female-biased adult sex ratio and higher mortality of calves and adults, especially in poor years, but his population will not necessarily oscillate between peaks and crashes. He may even see some increase in annual mortality as an advantage if he aims to encourage populations of predators or scavengers, like golden eagles or ravens, on his ground.

The difficulty faced by managers of Highland red deer populations is that they commonly combine elements of several of these hypothetical managers. Many would like to shoot large numbers of well-grown stags, maximize total venison production and minimize the impact of deer on forestry or adjoining farmland. Unfortunately, these aims conflict and managers consequently need to establish their own priorities for management.

Though ecological considerations may be involved in this decision, they are likely to be of less importance than economic and aesthetic ones[47]. Herbivore populations undisturbed by hunters or predators can be expected to grow until the rate of production of edible forage equals the rate at which it is consumed by the animals and their birth rate equals their death rate. Caughley[33] refers to this point as 'ecological carrying capacity' but it is not the only possible equilibrium, for offtake of animals by hunters or predators can maintain population density at a variety of lower levels. These will be associated with increased standing crops of vegetation (see Figure 8.9) as well as with increased growth and reproductive performance of individuals. The number of animals that must be killed each year to maintain animal numbers at a particular level will usually be highest at some point between half and three quarters of the ecological carrying capacity. However, this density will usually be substantially higher than the density at which the growth of individuals is maximized. The important point to grasp is that although different animal densities will have different consequences for individual growth, offtake and vegetation, no particular density is necessarily superior to any other[47]. On scientific grounds, none of the five options for managing Highland deer populations is inherently superior to any of the others and it is the manager's responsibility to decide between them. The best service the scientist can perform is to make this clear.

We dwell briefly on this point for some scientists have argued that regimes that maximize the growth and reproductive performance of individuals by maintaining a population density substantially below the level which the environment could sustain (the position of our third deer manager) are superior to other policies[48]. This position is commonly associated with the mistaken view that higher densities necessarily represent overpopulation[49] and that regular culling is 'an ecological duty applied with sorrow and reluctance for the greater good of the population and its habitat'[33].

Three reasons why culling regimes that hold population density well below the level it would reach in unculled populations are superior are often suggested: first, that they prevent drastic oscillations in population size associated with overgrazing and catastrophic mortality that would occur if populations were not culled; second, that they are more natural since in communities where predators are present they maintain herbivore numbers well below the potential carrying capacity of the environment; and third,

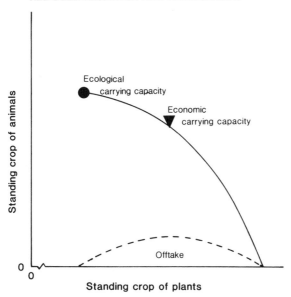

Figure 8.9 The zero isocline of vegetation marking the position of all equilibria between plants and animals enforceable by hunting. The offtake curve is the number of animals that must be killed annually to enforce each equilibrium. Ecological carrying capacity is the equilibrium point marking long-term average density of plants and animals in the absence of hunting. Economic carrying capacity is the point at which offtake is maximised, usually at an animal density of between half and three-quarters of ecological carrying capacity[33].

that they reduce natural mortality and have important humanitarian benefits.

There is little *scientific* basis for any of these three arguments. As we have already described, lightly culled or unculled populations are not necessarily unstable nor are they necessarily associated with ir-reversible damage to plant populations[9,32,48], for while some species are adversely affected by high grazing pressure, others benefit from it (see Chapter 4). High population densities of herbivores will certainly have some impact on local plant populations (see Figure 8.9) but whether this is regarded as undesirable, tolerable or desirable depends on the aims of managers.

Also, it is not yet clear how commonly predators *do* limit herbi-vore numbers nor, where this is the case, how far below the carrying capacity of the environment they hold them[9,23-26]. In communities where predators are abundant, like the Serengeti plains of Tanzania, starvation of ungulates is not uncommon[23,24]. Moreover, even if, in undisturbed communities, predators usually *did* hold herbivore numbers substantially below carrying capacity, there is no scientific reason why management should necessarily adopt this objective.

Finally, while culling regimes that minimize natural mortality may reduce animal suffering, it is important to appreciate that this is a philosophical argument rather than a biological one. We doubt that it is taken as seriously as is sometimes suggested for the same argument should stress the importance of culling garden birds and rodents (whose densities are commonly limited by food availability[50]) and of encouraging predators in pheasant coverts and on grouse moors.

Failure to distinguish scientific arguments from what Caughley[33] has called 'ecological theology' confuses the roles of scientist and manager, generating mutual misunderstandings. The proper brief of the wildlife scientist is to investigate and advise on the consequences of different management practices. In some cases, certain management options *will* be superior to others on true scientific grounds – for example, where the survival or integrity of species are concerned. However, where decisions depend primarily on economic, philosophical or aesthetic grounds, the scientist's role should be to inform the manager of the range of possible options, to advise him of their consequences, and then to leave him to decide his own priorities.

When the aims of management and the desired level of population density have been decided, it is possible to consider what size and distribution of cull are necessary to achieve them. Where the aim is to remove resident deer populations, the concentration of culling on mature hinds and young stags may be the quickest way to achieve this. Conversely, where the aim is to stablize population density while maximizing the annual harvest either of stags or of venison, it becomes necessary to estimate the culling rate that hind and stag populations can sustain. As we have already argued, this may vary from less than 10% of adults counted in spring to over 20%, depending on fecundity and juvenile survival. All methods of calculating the culling rate that populations can sustain rely on accurate measures of population size and recruitment which are seldom cheap or easy to collect[41,43]. We believe that the best advice that can be given to deer managers is to operate by trial and error, adopting a cull of a fixed size for several years and monitoring the effects on deer numbers by regular counts.

In summary, a range of different options is available to managers of Highland red deer populations and decisions on which to take are likely to depend more on economic or aesthetic criteria than on scientific ones. Once the aims of management have been defined, the wildlife scientist can advise on how these are most likely to be achieved. However, the dynamics of red deer populations vary locally and precise calculations of the maximum harvest that can be sustained depend on measures of population size, recruitment, mortality and dispersal of each sex. The variables are usually difficult to measure and, under most conditions, managers have the best chance of achieving their objectives by a systematic policy of trial and error, combined with a system for monitoring changes in the number of deer using their ground.

8.5 SUMMARY

8.1-8.3 Variation in population density, recruitment and survival in Highland red deer are closely related, both to each other and to measures of environmental quality. However, there are still large gaps in our understanding of the dynamics of Highland deer populations. Unanswered questions include: How does the density of hinds versus stags affect recruitment? How does population density affect dispersal? At what time of year are resources limiting? What factors affect the relative stability of populations? And how do different culling regimes affect growth, survival and reproductive performance and natural mortality?

8.4 Managers of Highland deer populations have to make two main decisions: what management objectives to aim for; and what population density to maintain. The optimal density of deer depends on the aims of management and is usually determined primarily by economic and aesthetic criteria, rather than by scientific ones. Where the aim of management is to maximize the number and quality of stags that can be shot, it is important that hind culls are large enough to hold population density below the ecological carrying capacity of the environment. Since the culling rate necessary to do this will vary, the most satisfactory way to determine the rate of culling that can be sustained may be to manipulate the size of the annual cull and to monitor the effects of this on population size. The practice of selecting hinds with poor calves and poorly grown stags is likely to be beneficial though the demographic and genetic consequences of selective culling may not be large.

REFERENCES

1. Fowler, C. H. (1987). 'A review of density dependence in populations of large mammals'. In: *Current Mammalogy* Vol. **1**, ed. H. H. Genoways, 401–441. Plenum Press, New York.
2. Albon, S. D. (1983). *Ecological Aspects of Growth, Reproduction and Mortality in Female Red Deer.* Ph.D. thesis, University of East Anglia.
3. Albon, S. D., Mitchell, B. & Staines, B. W. (1983). 'Fertility and body

weight in red deer: a density dependent relationship'. *J. Anim. Ecol.*, **52**, 969–980.

4. Clutton-Brock, T. H., Major, M., Albon, S. D. & Guinness, F. E. (1987). 'Early development and population dynamics in red deer. I. Density dependent effects of birth weight and date'. *J. Anim. Ecol.*, **56**, 56–67.

5. Skogland, T. (1983). 'The effects of density dependent resource limitation on size in wild reindeer'. *Oecologia*, **60**, 156–168.

6. Clutton-Brock, T. H. & Albon, S. D. (1985). 'Competition and population regulation in social mammals'. In: *Behavioural Ecology*, eds. R. M. Sibly & R. H. Smith, 557–576, Blackwells, Oxford.

7. Clutton-Brock, T. H., Albon, S. D. & Guinness, F. E. (1982). 'Competition between female relatives in a matrilineal mammal'. *Nature*, **350**, 178–180.

8. Clutton-Brock, T. H., Albon, S. D. & Guinness, F. E. (1987). 'Interactions between population density and maternal characteristics affecting juvenile survival in red deer'. *J. Anim. Ecol.*, **56**, 857–871.

9. Caughley, G. (1976b). 'Wildlife management and the dynamics of ungulate populations'. In: *Applied Biology*, ed. T. H. Coaker, 183–246. Academic Press, London.

10. Clutton-Brock, T. H., Albon, S. D. & Guinness, F. E. (1985). 'Parental investment and sex differences in juvenile mortality in birds and mammals'. *Nature*, **313**, 131–133.

11. Clutton-Brock, T. H. & Harvey, P. H. (1982). 'The functional significance of variation in body size in mammals'. In: *Mammal Behavior and Ecology*, ed. J. F. Eisenberg, 632–658. Smithsonian Publications, Washington.

12. Clutton-Brock, T. H., Iason, G. R. & Guinness, F. E. (1987). 'Sexual segregation and density-related changes in habitat use in male and female red deer (*Cervus elaphus*)'. *J. Zool.*, **211**, 275–289.

13. Illius, A. W. & Gordon, I. J. (1987). 'The allometry of food intake in grazing ruminants'. *J. Anim. Ecol.*, **56**, 989–1500.

14. Fordham, R. H. (1971). 'Field populations of *Peromyscus* with supplemented food'. *Ecology*, **52**, 138–146.

15. Hansen, L. P. & Batzli, G. O. (1978). 'The influence of food availability on the white footed mouse: populations in isolated woodlots'. *J. Mammal.*, **60**, 335–342.

16. Galindo, C. & Krebs, C. J. (1987). 'Population regulation in deer mice: the role of females'. *J. Anim. Ecol.*, **56**, 11–23.

17. Georgii, B. von & Schröder, W. (1978). 'Radiotelemetrisch gemessene Aktivatät weilblichen Rotwildes (*Cervus elaphus* L.)'. *Z. Jagdwiss.*, **24**, 9–23.

18. Georgii, B. von (1980). 'Home range patterns of female red deer (*Cervus elaphus* L.) in the Alps'. *Oecologia*, **47**, 278–285.

19. Catt, D. C. & Staines, B. W. (1987). 'Home range use and habitat selection by red deer (*Cervus elaphus*) in a Sitka spruce plantation as determined by radio-tracking'. *J. Zool.*, **211**, 618–693.

20. Greenwood, P. (1980). 'Mating systems, philopatry and dispersal in birds and mammals'. *Anim. Behav.*, **28**, 1140–1162.

21. Iason, G. R., Duck, C. D. & Clutton-Brock, T. H. (1986). 'Grazing and reproductive success in red deer: the effect of local enrichment by gull colonies'. *J. Anim. Ecol.*, **55**, 507–515.

22. *Red Deer Commission Report for 1959/60*. Red Deer Commission, Inverness.

23. Sinclair, A. R. E. (1977). *The Buffalo: a Study of Resource Limitation of Populations*. University of Chicago Press, Chicago.

24. Sinclair, A. R. E. & Norton Griffiths, M. (eds.) (1979). *Serengeti: Dynamics of an Ecosystem*. University of Chicago Press, Chicago.

25. Sinclair, A. R. E., Dublin, H. & Borner, M. (1985). 'Population regulation of Serengeti wildebeest: a test of the food hypothesis'. *Oecologia*, **65**, 266–268.

26. Sinclair, A. R. E. (1985). 'Does interspecific competition or predation shape the African ungulate communities?'. *J. Anim. Ecol.*, **54**, 899–918.

27. Leader-Williams, N. (1988). *Reindeer in South Georgia: the Ecology of an Introduced Population*. Cambridge University Press, Cambridge.

28. Skogland, T. (1985). 'The effects of density-dependent resource limitations on the demography of wild reindeer'. *J. Anim. Ecol.*, **54**, 359–374.

29. Caughley, G. (1970). 'Eruption of ungulate populations, with emphasis on Himalayan thar in New Zealand'. *Ecology*, **51**, 53–72.

30. Jewell, P. A., Milner, C. & Morton Boyd, J. (1974). *Island Survivors: the Ecology of the Soay Sheep of St. Kilda*. Athlone Press, London.

31. Klein, D. R. (1968). 'The introduction, increase and crash of reindeer on St. Mathew Island'. *J. Wildl. Mgmt.*, **34**, 353–367.

32. Caughley, G. (1976). 'Plant-herbivore systems'. In: *Theoretical Ecology: Principles and Applications*, ed. R. M. May, 94–113. Blackwells, Oxford.

33. Caughley, G. (1979). 'What is this thing called carrying capacity?' In: *North American Elk*, eds. M. S. Boyce & L. D. Hayden-Wing, 2–8. University of Wyoming Press, Laramie.

34. Houston, D. B. (1982). *The Northern Yellowstone Elk*. Macmillans, New York.

35. Taber, R. D., Raedeke, K. & McCaughran, D. A. (1982). 'Population characteristics'. In: *Elk of North America*, eds. J. W. Thomas & D. E. Toweill, 279–300. Stackpole Books, Harrisburg, Pennsylvania.

36. Sauer, J. R. & Boyce, M. J. (1983). 'Density-dependence and survival

of elk in Northwestern Wyoming'. *J. Wildl. Mgmt.*, **47**, 31–37.

37. Picton, H. D. (1984). 'Climate and the prediction of reproduction of three ungulate species'. *J. Appl. Ecol.*, **21**, 869–879.

38. Sobanskii, G. G. (1979). 'Selective elimination in the Siberian stag population in the Altais as a result of the early winter of 1976/77'. *Soviet J. Ecol.*, **10**, 78–80. Translated from Russian, Consultants Bureau, New York.

39. Beddington, J. R. (1973). *The Exploitation of Red Deer (Cervus elaphus L.) in Scotland*. Ph.D. thesis, University of Edinburgh.

40. Beddington, J. R. (1975). 'Age structure, sex ratio and population density in harvesting of natural animal populations'. *J. Appl.Ecol.*, **11**, 915–924.

41. Beddington, J. R. (1975). 'Economic and ecological analysis of red deer harvesting in Scotland'. *J. Environ. Mgmt.*, **3**, 91–103.

42. MacNab, J. (1985). 'Carrying capacity and related slippery shibboleths'. *Wildl. Soc. Bull.*, **13**, 403–410.

43. Caughley, G. (1977). *Analysis of Vertebrate Populations*. John Wiley, London.

44. Lowe, V. P. W. (1969). 'Population dynamics of the red deer (*Cervus elaphus* L.) on Rhum'. *J. Anim. Ecol.*, **38**, 425–457.

45. Lowe, V. P. W. (1971). 'Some effects of a change in estate management on a deer population'. In: *The Scientific Management of Animal and Plant Communities*, eds. E. Duffey & A. S. Watt, 437–456. Blackwells, Oxford.

46. Red Deer Commission (1981). *Red Deer Management*. H.M.S.O., Edinburgh.

47. Bell, R. H. V. (1983). 'Decision making in wildlife management with reference to problems of over-population'. In: *Management of Large Mammals in African Conservation Areas*, ed. R. N. Owen-Smith, 145–172. Haum, Pretoria.

48. Dasmann, W. (1971). *If Deer are to Survive*. Stackpole Books, Harrisburg, Pennsylvania.

49. Caughley, G. (1981). 'Over-population'. In: *Problems in Management of Locally Abundant Mammals*, eds. P. A. Jewell and S. J. Holt, 7–19. Academic Press, London.

50. Lack, D. (1954). *The Natural Regulation of Animal Numbers*. Clarendon, Oxford.

Appendix 1
The Accuracy of Deer Counts

When counting sizeable populations of any animal in broken country, it is likely that some groups will be missed while others may be counted twice. Most attempts to estimate population densities of large mammals suffer from very limited accuracy – systematic or unsystematic errors of 25%, or even 50%, are not uncommon[1,2,3]. In comparison, assessments of the accuracy of the Red Deer Commission's counts suggest that this is unusually high.

Four independent attempts have been made to investigate the consistency or accuracy of the Red Deer Commission's counts, all based on Rhum. Following the spring count of Rhum in 1974, Lincoln[4] counted the entire island over a seven-day period in October. Comparison of the number of animals he saw in the North Block with the known number of recognisable individuals using the block (see Chapter 1) suggested that he missed around 15% of all animals. Assuming this to be the case and allowing for known recruitment and mortality between spring and autumn, Lincoln's estimates suggest a total population of 1428 animals with a sex ratio of 95.2 stags to 100 hinds. This compares closely with the Commission's estimate of 1438 animals with a sex ratio of 96.9 stags to 100 hinds.

A second method of checking counting consistency is to compare the number of animals counted in a year with the number expected from the previous season's count, less the number of animals killed or dying naturally and the number of animals born within the year. If the count is accurate and most natural mortality is found, the number of animals counted should tally closely with the number expected. Comparisons of the number of animals counted on Rhum by the Nature Conservancy's stalkers between 1958 and 1966 show that expected and observed numbers of deer were similar, differing by an average of less than 1.0% of the total with a range of -5.6 to $+3.8$% (Table A.1.1). Between 1980 and 1986 when the counts were carried out by the Red Deer Commission, discrepancies ranged from -6.6 to $+1.5$% with a mean of -4.1% (Table A.1.1).

Table A.1.1   The numbers of adult red deer counted in spring on Rhum each year compared with the number expected from the previous year's count less all known mortality (number culled + number found dead) for two periods. The percentage difference is calculated as $\frac{\text{Counted} - \text{Expected}}{\text{Expected}}$ Counts from 1958–1965 were carried out by the Nature Conservancy's stalkers, those for 1980–1986 by the Red Deer Commission. (Data from references 5 and 6 and N.C.C. unpublished records.)

Year	Count	Expected	% difference	Year	Count	Expected	% difference
1958	1416	1425	− 0.6	1980	1147	1228	− 6.6
1959	1497	1442	+ 3.8	1981	1155	1201	− 3.8
1960	1486	1431	+ 3.8	1981	1157	1261	− 8.2
1961	1505	1521	− 1.1	1983	1104	1179	− 6.4
1962	1458	1449	+ 0.6	1984	1191	1173	+ 1.5
1963	1443	1411	+ 2.3	1985	1232	1263	− 2.5
1964	1489	1434	+ 3.8	1986	1267	1304	− 2.8
1965	1461	1548	− 5.6				
Mean	1469	1457	+ 0.87	Mean	1179	1230	− 4.1

As tests of counting accuracy, both independent counts and comparisons of observed and expected numbers have their drawbacks for they will not necessarily reveal systematic counting errors. For example, if deer numbers were always underestimated by 20% each year, counts by different observers might still agree reasonably well. Comparisons of observed and expected numbers suffer from the same limitations. In addition, they have the disadvantage that the counting team could have an expectation of population size.

One way of estimating the true accuracy of counts is to reconstruct the population present in a given year by estimating the ages of all animals shot or dying naturally[5]. For example, if we know that all deer live for less than 20 years and we age all animals shot or dying naturally over a twenty-year period in a self-contained population, we can determine the population size in the first year by adding up the number of animals born in that year that died in each successive season. In practice, it is not necessary to continue to monitor mortality over the maximum lifespan and an accurate estimate of population size can be obtained as soon as a high proportion of the original animals are known to have died.

This method was used by Lowe to check the accuracy of the Nature Conservancy's counts on Rhum between 1957 and 1962[5,6] and by ourselves to check the accuracy of the Red Deer Commission's counts in 1971, 1972 and 1974. Lowe's comparisons indicate that the total number of deer counted by the Nature Conservancy exceeded the reconstructed population by an average of 3%,

Table A.1.2   Comparisons between the Nature Conservancy's counts of deer on Rhum, 1957–1962, and the population reconstructed by aging animals shot or dying naturally (from Reference 6, Table 2). Differences show the extent to which the count was higher or lower than the reconstructed population.

Year		Stags	Hinds	Calves	Total
1957	Counted	564	741	279	1584
	Reconstructed	627	647	262	1536
	Difference (animals)	− 63	+ 94	+ 17	+ 48
	% difference	− 10.0	+ 14.5	+ 6.5	+ 3.1
1958	Counted	598	818	295	1711
	Reconstructed	664	708	258	1630
	Difference (animals)	− 66	+ 110	− 37	+ 81
	% difference	− 10.7 *-9.9%*	+ 15.5	− 14.3	+ 4.9
1959	Counted	626	871	236	1733
	Reconstructed	667	694	337	1698
	Difference (animals)	− 44	+ 179	− 101	− 35
	% difference	− 6.2	+ 25.5	− 30.0	− 2.1
1960	Counted	624	862	314	1800
	Reconstructed	706	696	340	1742
	Difference (animals)	− 82	+ 116	− 86	+ 38
	% difference	− 11.6	+ 23.8 *16·6% +*	− 7.6 *-25·2%*	+ 3.3
1961	Counted	669	824	319	1812
	Reconstructed	761	708	302	1771
	Difference (animals)	− 92	+ 116	+ 17	+ 41
	% difference	− 12.1	+ 16.4	+ 5.6	+ 2.3
1962	Counted	709	719	274	1702
	Reconstructed	728	585	258	1561
	Difference(animals)	− 19	+ 134	+ 26	+ 141
	% difference	− 2.6	+ 22.9	+ 10.1	+ 9.0
	Mean % difference:	− 8.9	+ 19.8	− 4.95	+ 3.4
	Range:	− 2.6 to − 12.1	+ 14.5 to + 25.5	− 30.0 to + 10.1	− 2.1 to + 9.0

though, in one year, the counted population exceeded the reconstructed estimate by 9% (see Table A.1.2). It is unsurprising that counted figures tended to exceed reconstructed numbers for it is likely that a proportion of animals dying naturally were never found. Our reconstructions of the Commission's counts also show that the total number of animals counted was very similar to the reconstructed population, differing by between − 2.9% and + 4.0% (Table A.1.3).

However, while the total numbers of deer counted on Rhum were similar to the size of the reconstructed populations, the relative numbers of stags, hinds and calves varied widely. Between 1957 and 1962, the Nature Conservancy's counts of stags were, on average, around 9% lower than the reconstructed population while hind

Table A.1.3   Comparisons between the Red Deer Commission's counts on Rhum in 1971, 1972 and 1974 and the population reconstructed by ageing animals shot or dying naturally. Differences show the extent to which the count was higher or lower than the reconstructed population. In years when mortality searches were not conducted we have estimated the number of animals that died using the relationship in Figure 6.17 and in these years, together with those where the records only specify the sex, we have distributed the mortality across age classes in the same proportions as the age-specific mortality between 1979–80 and 1986–87. These estimates were necessary to permit the reconstruction but have a negligible effect on the final value. For example, if we assumed no animals died in the years with incomplete records the reconstructed values for stags would only decline by between 4 and 8 individuals.

	Stags	Hinds	Calves	Total
1971 Counted	492	509	174	1175
Reconstruction	621	388	201	1210
Difference (animals)	− 129	+ 121	− 27	− 35
% difference	− 20.8	+ 31.2	− 13.4	− 2.9
1972 Count	537	624	231	1392
Reconstruction	648	467	224	1339
Difference (animals)	− 111	+ 157	+ 7	+ 53
% difference	− 17.1	+ 33.6	+ 3.1	+ 4.0
1974 Count	585	604	249	1438
Reconstruction	668	531	*	*
Difference (animals)	− 83	+ 73	*	*
% difference	− 12.4	+ 13.2	*	*
Mean % difference	− 16.7	+ 26.0	− 5.2	+ 0.5
Range	− 20.8 to − 12.4	+ 13.2 to + 33.6	− 13.4 to + 3.1	− 2.9 to + 4.0

*These figures could not be estimated since a proportion of these calves may still be alive.

numbers were around 20% higher. Differences in calf numbers were large but inconsistent, ranging from − 30% to + 10% (see Table A.1.2). Comparisons between the Red Deer Commission's counts on Rhum for 1971, 1972 and 1974 and our reconstructions of the population based on the ages of animals killed or dying naturally show the same trends: over the three years counted, the numbers of stags counted were consistently lower than reconstructed numbers while the numbers of hinds counted were consistently higher.

Lowe's interpretation of his results was that a proportion of poor yearling males (knobbers) and well-grown calves were classified as hinds[5,6]. An alternative interpretation is that the counts were accurate but that the reconstruction was at fault. However it is not easy to see how this can explain the consistently *lower numbers of stags* in counted versus reconstructed populations. If a substantial proportion of knobbers were missed, as Lowe suggests, it seems most likely that this was because they were classified as hinds and that hind numbers were consequently over-estimated.

We believe that two conclusions should be drawn from these

Table A.1.4   Census, cull and mortality estimates for hinds at Glenfeshie based on Red Deer Commission counts 1967–1973[8].

Year	Spring census		No. removed		Spring census next year			
	Hind	Calves*	Cull	Mort.	Obs.	Expected†	Difference‡	% difference counted − expected / expected
1967	807	146	72	24	1068	857	+ 211	+ 24.6
1968	1068	181	159	31	982	1059	− 77	− 7.3
1969	982	184	263	43	1224	860	+ 364	+ 42.3
1970	1224	227	182	25	1190	1244	− 54	− 4.3
1971	1190	221	151	23	1000	1237	− 237	− 19.2
1972	1000	162	164	10	897	988	− 91	− 9.2
1973	897	186	174	43	1160	866	+ 294	+ 33.9

*Female calves assumed on basis of 50:50 sex ratio of number of calves counted.
†Expected in spring based on previous April estimate minus number culled and dying naturally.
‡Difference equals observed minus expected.

attempts to assess the accuracy of deer counts. First, that estimates of total deer numbers are likely to be reasonably accurate. Any errors that exist are most unlikely to be large enough to generate the substantial differences in population density found throughout the Highlands.

Second, that the available evidence suggests that considerable misclassification may have occurred both in the Nature Conservancy's counts and in subsequent Red Deer Commission counts on Rhum. Though it is not known to what extent these differences occur on the Scottish mainland, we believe that estimates of the ratio of calves to hinds or of hinds to stags should be interpreted cautiously.

One final caveat. While estimates of total deer numbers in substantial areas, like the counting blocks (see Figure 2.1), may be accurate, individual counts of particular deer forests or research blocks may be unrepresentative owing to temporary differences in the distribution of deer in response to weather or disturbance. Only repeated counts of the same area will remove error of this kind. In addition, regular seasonal movements may have important effects – a problem that is well illustrated by counts at Glenfeshie. Until the early 1970s, a large number of hinds moved on to the estate in the early summer and left again in the autumn[7]. However, the numbers of hinds involved varied widely between years with the result that the number of hinds counted on Glenfeshie in spring differed from the number expected (based on the previous year's count plus new calves less winter mortality) by between − 19% and + 42% (Table A.1.4).

REFERENCES

1. Caughley, G. (1977). *Analysis of Vertebrate Populations*. Wiley, Chichester.
2. Norton Griffiths, M. (1976). *Counting Animals*. Handbook No.1. African Wildlife Leadership Foundation, Nairobi.
3. Western, D. & Grimsdell, J. S. R. (1979). *Measuring the Distribution of Animals in Relation to the Environment*. Handbook No. 2. African Wildlife Leadership Foundation, Nairobi.
4. Lincoln, G.A. (1975). 'A deer count on Rhum in October'. *Deer*, 3, 337–338.
5. Lowe, V. P. W. (1969). 'Population dynamics of the red deer (*Cervus elaphus* L.) on Rhum'. *J. Anim. Ecol.*, 38, 425–457.
6. Lowe, V. P. W. (1971). 'Some effects of a change in estate management on a deer population'. In: *The Scientific Management of Animal and Plant Communities for Conservation*, eds. E. Duffey & A. S. Watt, 437–456, Blackwells, Oxford.
7. Staines, B., Personal communication.
8. Mitchell, B., McCowan, D. & Parish, T. (1986). 'Performance and population dynamics in relation to management of red deer *Cervus elaphus* at Glenfeshie, Inverness-shire, Scotland'. *Biological Conservation*, 37, 237–267.

Appendix 2
Estimating Variation in Deer Density: the Block-year Model

A.2.1 GENERAL DESCRIPTION OF MODEL

Estimating spatial and temporal variation in deer density is complex because representative samples of ground have not been covered regularly (see Chapter 2). Our analysis is limited to whole blocks, or parts of larger blocks, in which deer have been counted at least twice (Table A.2.1) since single counts do not permit extrapolation. An intuitive approach to the problem is to plot a graph of the observed densities for each block or parish in each year that it was counted and then to connect consecutive counts by a straight line. Having calculated the change in density per year for each block we could average the values across all blocks for each year producing an estimate of the average change in deer density. However, one weakness of this approach is that it assumes a linear change during the intervals between counts with the risk that in a fluctuating population two counts several years apart may completely miss a trough or peak between them. Because of the inherent problems of this approach we have adopted a more rigorous statistical method using multiple regression techniques. The basic model used estimated density from an equation including both year and block identity as independent variables. Since blocks varied in area by an order of magnitude we decided that blocks should not have equal weight in the analysis of density and weighted values in the model by the area of each block. This model allowed us to estimate the temporal variation in deer density controlling for variation in the density of different blocks, and to estimate the spatial variation in deer density controlling for temporal fluctuations, as if all the blocks had been sampled in the same year. Spatial and temporal variation in the size of the cull was analysed using the block-year model.

Table A.2.1   Years in which different blocks were counted by the Red Deer Commission.

Count blocks	Count years
1. N. Sutherland	1986*
2. Caithness/Suth'land	1963, 1964*, 1966*, 1970*, 1973*, 1975*, 1986
3. W. Sutherland	1976, 1981*
4. E. Sutherland	1964, 1979
5. Wester Ross	1966*, 1975
6. North Ross	1962, 1968, 1984
7. Rovie/Skibo	—
8. Gairloch Cons. Unit	1973, 1978, 1981
9. Applecross	1965
10. Shieldaig/Ledgowan	1974
11. South Ross	1965, 1969, 1973, 1984
12. Glenmoriston/Glenurquhart	1974
13. W. Inverness-shire	1972, 1974*, 1985
14. Ardochy/Port Clair	1974
15. W. Loch Shiel	1970, 1983
16. Ardnamurchan	1967, 1983
17. Conaglen/Ardgour	1967, 1975, 1980, 1985
18. Morvern	1971, 1977, 1980, 1982, 1986
19. Monadhliaths	1968, 1977
20. Cabrach/Glen Fiddich	1965, 1966, 1967
21. Cairngorm/W. Grampians	1961*, 1962*, 1963*, 1964*, 1965*, 1966*, 1967, 1983
22. Ben Nevis/Blackmount	1970, 1978, 1982*
23. Corrour/Ben Alder/Ardverikie	1968, 1972, 1978, 1986
24. E. Loch Ericht	1970, 1972, 1977, 1978, 1980, 1985
25. E. Grampians	1966, 1975, 1979, 1986
26. Rannoch/S. Tay	1961*, 1967*, 1979
27. S. Loch Tay	1986*
28. Argyll	1980*, 1981*
29. Trossachs	1981*
30. Glenartney	1971, 1975, 1979, 1986
31. Galloway	—
32. Harris/Lewis	1982
33. N. Uist	1980, 1985
34. Skye	1980
35. Scalpay	—
36. Rhum	1961–1986, except 1969 and 1973
37. Mull	1962*, 1969*, 1971*, 1979, 1986*
38. Scarba	1973
39. Jura	1965, 1969, 1972, 1978
40. Islay	1963, 1974*
41. Arran	1968, 1971, 1979, 1981

*Part of block

Table A.2.2   The number of blocks covered in each year included in the model.

Year	No. blocks covered	Year	No. blocks covered	Year	No. blocks covered
1961	3	1970	6	1979	9
1962	4	1971	5	1980	5
1963	5	1972	6	1981	4
1964	4	1973	3	1982	3
1965	5	1974	2	1983	5
1966	6	1975	7	1984	3
1967	7	1976	2	1985	5
1968	5	1977	4	1986	9
1969	4	1978	7		
				Mean	4.8

A.2.2   THE DATA

(1)   The block-year model

The data used in the model came from 28 Red Deer Commission blocks with at least two counts (Table A.2.1). In five of these blocks, Caithness/East Sutherland, West Inverness-shire, Cairngorm/West Grampian, Ben Nevis/Blackmount and Mull, large parts were counted on one occasion and not another. We have, therefore, split these blocks, giving a total of 33 blocks in the model. These samples were distributed such that in every year there were at least two counts, with up to nine in some years (Table A.2.2). In all there were 128 block-year values. All count data were converted to density values (deer per km^2) where the area of blocks was measured from Ordnance Survey 1:50,000 maps. Tracts of water, forestry and agricultural land from which deer were excluded were subtracted from the total area.

Information on the number of deer culled was less complete and estimates of temporal and spatial variation in the cull were based on 116 block-year values. Average numbers culled were calculated for the three years immediately prior to the count because the size of the cull in particular blocks varied between years and the average numbers should have reflected longer term trends more accurately than individual years. For example, in 1967 the Conaglen/Ardgour block was counted. We inspected the cull returns for all estates in this block for the three years immediately prior to the count (1964/5, 1965/6 and 1966/7). Where the cull records were incomplete for an estate, it was discarded from the data and also removed from the 1967 count data. For each estate with complete records between

1964/5 and 1966/7, we calculated an average annual cull. These values were totalled and then expressed as:

(1) The number of deer culled per unit area (km^2) where the area of the block was the total of the individual estates with complete returns.

(2) A percentage cull of the autumn population assuming no winter mortality (average number culled divided by average number culled plus number counted in the winter/spring of 1967).

(2) The parish-year model

In order to investigate possible within-block variation in density we aggregated the counts of individual estates and calculated densities for the parishes within each of the Commission's count blocks. We chose parishes because they were generally larger than estates, they commonly follow major topographical features such as watersheds, and they may contain relatively discrete populations. Many of the larger blocks included several parishes, but some parishes crossed the boundary of two blocks. In some cases, these were covered in different years and therefore it was necessary to subdivide some parishes. In all, we defined 108 parish units with two or more deer counts and in the parish-year model had 384 parish-year values.

A.2.3 ANALYSIS

(1) The basic block-year model

All the block-year and parish-year models were analysed by multiple regression techniques using procedures in the GENSTAT statistical package[1]. As we describe above, the data were from blocks or parishes counted at least twice. The simple model used was

$$\text{estimated density} = y_i = \mu + \alpha_{b(i)} + \beta_{t(i)} + \varepsilon_i \tag{1}$$

where μ is an overall mean value (constant),
$b(i)$ is the block corresponding to the i'th value,
$t(i)$ is the year corresponding to the i'th value.

Since the blocks were not all covered the same number of times, differed in area by more than an order of magnitude and had populations of different size, the assumption of equal error variances was not valid. Therefore, we chose to weight the values in the model by the area of each block or parish[2]. An alternative weighting system using the square root of the number of deer counted gave similar estimates of the temporal variation[3] in population size.

(2) Approximation of temporal variation: polynomial curve fitting

The basic block-year model does not assume that the values for adjacent years are more likely to be similar than in years with a large time separation, even though the temporal variation is likely to take the form of a smooth curve. One way to deal with this in the model is to fit a polynomial in time instead of estimating the separate year values.

In equation (1) we replace $\beta_{t(i)}$ to give

$$y_i = \mu + \alpha_{b(i)} + \gamma_1(t_{(i)} - t_o) + \ldots + \gamma_p(t_{(i)} - t_o)_p + \varepsilon_i \tag{2}$$

where t_o is an arbitrary base year and p is the maximal degree of polynomial to be considered. Thus, the new model is *nested* within the old one, and the two may be compared by first removing the *block effect*. If the temporal variation remaining after fitting the polynomial curve is significant, it suggests that there is some genuine deviation from the polynomial which is not random error.

(3) Within-block variation and block-year interactions

The block-year model assumes that the variation between blocks is greater than the variation within them. This can be tested by using the results from the block-year and parish-year models because the model for observations at the parish level

$$y'_{(j)} = \alpha'_{p(j)} + \beta_{t(j)} + \varepsilon_j \tag{3}$$

where $p_{(j)}$ is the parish corresponding to the jth observation is equivalent to

$$y'_{(j)} = \alpha_{b(j)} + (\alpha'_{1p(j)} - \alpha'_{b(j)}) + \beta_{t(j)} + \varepsilon_j \tag{4}$$

$$= \alpha_{b(j)} + \sigma_{p(j)} + \beta_{t(j)} + \varepsilon_j \qquad (5)$$

where $b_{(j)}$ is the block of the jth parish

permitting straightforward decomposition into between and within-block components after removing the *year effects* in an analysis of variance table as follows:

Sums of squares	Degrees of freedom
Due to blocks	No. of blocks − 1
Due to parishes	No. of parishes − no. of blocks
Residual SS (1) from block model	No. of values in block model − degrees of freedom due to year and blocks
Residual SS (2) by subtraction	By subtraction
Total SS from parish model (after removing years)	No. of parish values − no. of years

The determination of the analysis of variance in the two models also permits us to test for the presence of a block-year interaction. This is checked by an F-test on the ratio of the mean sums of squares from residual (1) and residual (2). A significant result would indicate that the pattern of temporal change differs from block to block. If the block-year interaction is not significant then the two residuals are pooled and used to test the within-block (parish) variation. However, even if the within-block variation is significant the between and within-block mean sums of squares may still be compared to see if the former is substantially greater.

A.2.4 RESULTS

(1) The basic block-year model

After removing block effects (spatial variation) the density of total deer, and both stags and hinds, differed significantly between years (Table A.2.3). Similarly, after accounting for the temporal variation, the differences between blocks were significant (Table A.2.3). The temporal and spatial factors associated with variation in deer density are described in Chapter 2. A more comprehensive coverage of the correlates of spatial and temporal variation are documented in Appendices 3 and 4.

Table A.2.3 Block-year regression models for total deer density, stag density, and hind density. In each case year effects were calculated after removal of block effects and vice versa. For complete decomposition of sums of squares see ref. 4.

	Total deer density			Stag density			Hind density		
	f-ratio	d.f.	*p*-value	*f*-ratio	d.f.	*p*-value	*f*-ratio	d.f.	*p*-value
Year effects	6.044	25,70	***	4.604	25,70	***	6.800	25,70	***
Block effects	28.351	32,70	***	23.705	32,70	***	25.730	32,70	***
% variance explained		90.4			89.0			89.8	

***$p<0.001$

Table A.2.4 Block-year regression model results for numbers culled per km² and % cull (separated by sex). In each case year effects were calculated after removal of block effects and vice versa. For complete decomposition of sums of squares see ref. 4.

	Number culled per km²					
	Stags			Hinds		
	f-ratio	d.f.	*p*-value	*f*-ratio	d.f.	*p*-value
Year effects	2.657	25,60	**	1.490	25,60	NS
Block effects	12.820	30,60	***	8.281	30,60	***

	% culled					
	Stags			Hinds		
	f-ratio	d.f.	*p*-value	*f*-ratio	d.f.	*p*-value
Year effects	3.296	25,60	***	3.819	25,60	***
Block effects	3.229	30,60	***	4.031	30,60	***

NS = not significant ** = $p<0.01$ *** = $p<0.001$

We used the same model to investigate both spatial and temporal variation in the cull. The number of deer culled per square kilometre varied between blocks in both sexes but only between years among stags (Table A.2.4). The between-block differences in numbers culled per square kilometre might have arisen simply because density varied across blocks. However, the percentage cull also differed between blocks in both stags and hinds (Table A.2.4). Consequently, when investigating the correlates of spatial variation in density (Chapter 2, Appendix 3) we chose to use the percentage of each sex culled. In contrast, when investigating the correlates of temporal variation in density, we chose to use numbers culled per square kilometre rather than percentage cull because the latter would have varied inversely with density if the number of deer culled was constant but population size fluctuated. As a result, negative correlations between temporal variation in density and the percentage cull are difficult to interpret.

Table A.2.5 Analysis of variance tables for tests of the fit of quartic polynomial curves fitted to the temporal variation (see Section A.2.3.2 for details) in (1) total density (2) stag density (3) hind density. In all models block effects were removed first.

(1) Total density

	Sums of squares	d.f.	Mean square	
1st degree term	63596	1	63596	
2nd degree term	6834	1	6834	
3rd degree term	4662	1	4662	
4th degree term	39084	1	39084	
Years	41292	21	1966.3	$F_{21,70} = 1.910, p<0.05$
Residual	72049	70	1029.3	

(2) Stag density

	Sums of squares	d.f.	Mean squares	
1st degree term	3593	1	3593	
2nd degree term	270	1	270	
3rd degree term	1210	1	1210	
4th degree term	4560	1	4560	
Years	7526	21	358.4	$F_{21,70} = 2.404, p<0.01$
Residual	10436	70	149.1	

(3) Hind density

	Sums of squares	d.f.	Mean square	
1st degree term	24547	1	24547	
2nd degree term	4950	1	4950	
3rd degree term	1273	1	1273	
4th degree term	8142	1	8142	
Years	9859	21	469.5	$F_{21,70} = 1.637, P<0.1$
Residual	20082	70	286.9	

(2) Polynomial curve fitting

The temporal variation remaining after fitting the polynomial curve was significant for total density and stag density (Table A.2.5). However, hind density was described adequately by a quartic polynomial of the form

$$y_i = 10.726 + \alpha_{b(i)} - 1.567x + 0.2244x^2 - 0.0117x^3 + 0.0002068x^4$$

where y_i = estimated density in block i in year x.

$\alpha_{b(i)}$ = constant for block i

x = year, where $1961 = 1$, $1962 = 2$, etc.

The fitted polynomial curve describing temporal variation in hind density is shown in Figure 2.2. Although there was significant year to year variation in total deer and stag density we chose to fit

Table A.2.6 Decomposition of the sums of squares from the block-year and parish-year models to test block-year interactions and within block variation in (1) total deer density (2) stag density (3) hind density. Analysis of variance table is based on total SS from parish model after removing year-effects.

(1) Total deer density

	Sums of squares	d.f.	Mean square	
Between blocks	933529	32	29172.8	
Between parishes (within blocks)	757563	75	10100.8	$F_{75,252} = 7.497, p<0.001$
Residual SS (1) (from block model)	72049	70	1029.3	$F_{70,182} = 0.700$, NS
Residual SS (2) (by subtraction)	267480	182	1469.7	
Total SS from parish model	2030621	359		

(2) Stag density

	Sums of squares	d.f.	Mean square	
Between blocks	113016	32	3532.0	
Between parishes (within blocks)	179359	75	2391.5	$F_{75,252} = 7.451, p<0.001$
Residual SS (1) (from block model)	10436	70	149.1	$F_{70,182} = 0.385$, NS
Residual SS (2) (by subtraction)	70450	182	387.1	
Total SS from parish model	373261	359		

(3) Hind density

	Sums of squares	d.f.	Mean square	
Between blocks	236239	32	7382.0	
Between parishes (within blocks)	229798	75	3064.0	$F_{75,252} = 7.07, p<0.001$
Residual SS (1) (from block model)	20082	70	286.9	$F_{70,182} = 0.586$, NS
Residual SS (2) (by subtraction)	89139	182	489.8	
Total SS from parish model	575258	359		

polynomial curves through the graphs of temporal variation in Chapter 2 as the best indicator of the trends in density.

(3) Within-block variation and block-year interactions

In all measures of density there were no significant block-year interactions (ratio of mean squares of residual SS(1) and residual SS(2): Table A.2.6). Therefore, the temporal change was similar across blocks and the two residuals were pooled and used to test the within-block (parish) variation. The between-parish variation was significant for total deer density, stag density and hind density (Table A.2.6). As a result, we chose to use the parish level in our investigation of the environmental correlates of deer density. Nonetheless, there is evidence that there is substantial geographical variation in density because the between-block and within-block ratio of mean squares was greater than two (equivalent to a 1% significance level) for total deer density and hind density.

A.2.5 CONCLUSIONS

The basic block-year model indicated that the densities of red deer varied significantly between the Commission's count blocks and across years between 1961 and 1986. Since there was no statistical interaction between blocks and years it appeared that temporal changes were similar across blocks. Since there was significant within-block variation at the parish level we investigated the correlates of spatial variation in density at the parish level rather than the block level (see Appendix 3).

Temporal variation in deer density was irregular and was only explained by a polynomial curve in the case of hinds. Though fluctuations in size of individual populations did not necessarily follow smooth trends (see Appendix 1), the large year to year fluctuations in average deer density may have arisen from the paucity of counts in any one year and the long intervals between repeat counts. More regular counts of smaller areas of ground would probably solve this problem. Despite this reservation the model provides a general description of temporal and spatial variation in deer density.

REFERENCES

1. Alvey, N., Galway, N. & Lane, P. (1982). *An Introduction to Genstat*. Academic Press, London.
2. Jacquest, S. (1984). *Temporal and Spatial Variation in the Population Density of Scottish Red Deer*. Diploma thesis, Department of Statistics, University of Cambridge.
3. Morris, R. (1986). *Spatial Variation in the Density of Red Deer in the Highlands*. Diploma thesis, Department of Statistics, University of Cambridge.

4. Clutton-Brock, T. H. & Albon, S. D. (1987). *Red Deer in the Highlands: the Ecology of a Marginal Population*. Unpublished report to the Red Deer Commission, Highlands & Islands Development Board and Rannoch Trust.

Appendix 3
Temporal Variation in Deer Density in the Highlands

A.3.1 INTRODUCTION

Since year to year changes in deer density must result from variation in births and deaths (including culling) one would ideally construct a model which included density-dependent and density-independent factors affecting age-specific fertility and mortality rates. Unfortunately, age-specific fertility and mortality rates are only available for a limited number of populations and we do not have a comprehensive understanding of how density-dependent effects vary in magnitude across populations or how they interact with density-independent factors to influence these vital rates. Consequently, we have only correlated the year estimates of density with climatic variables that might be associated with annual variation in performance (see Chapter 6) together with changes in culling rates and sheep stocks.

A.3.2 MATERIALS AND METHODS

(1) Estimated deer density

The year estimates of density were calculated using the block-year model (see Appendix 2). However, as we described in Chapter 2, we have reservations about the magnitude of changes in estimated density between consecutive years. A 40% increase in density between two years must almost certainly arise from error due to the infrequent counts of Blocks which vary in density by up to ten-fold. Consequently, we have chosen to use the fitted polynomial curve (see Appendix 2) to estimate the density each year (see Table A.3.1). Although this method introduced a potential problem with autocorrelation, a previous analysis using the actual year estimates from the block-year model gave similar results[1].

Table A.3.1 Estimated total deer, stag and hind density (per km²) for each year between 1961 and 1986. Two types of estimate are given for each category, one from the block-year model and the other from the fitted polynomial curve (see Appendix 1). In addition we list the deviations between the two estimates (deviation = block-year estimate − polynomial estimate).

	Estimated total density (per km²)			Estimated stag density (per km²)			Estimated hind density (per km²)		
	Block-year model (1)	Polynomial model (2)	Deviation between (1) & (2)	Block-year model (3)	Polynomial model (4)	Deviation between (3) & (4)	Block-year model (5)	Polynomial model (6)	Deviation between (5) & (6)
1961	10.06	11.57	−1.51	2.69	3.38	−0.69	5.28	5.97	−0.69
1962	9.15	9.61	−0.46	2.71	2.75	−0.04	4.82	4.99	−0.17
1963	9.82	8.34	1.48	2.91	2.36	0.55	5.19	4.34	0.85
1964	8.57	7.61	0.96	2.54	2.16	0.38	4.24	3.95	0.29
1965	8.78	7.31	1.47	2.64	2.11	0.53	4.44	3.76	0.68
1966	5.65	7.35	−1.70	1.73	2.17	−0.44	2.70	3.74	−1.04
1967	7.90	7.62	0.28	2.47	2.30	0.17	3.91	3.83	0.08
1968	6.56	8.04	−1.48	1.91	2.49	−0.58	3.49	4.00	−0.51
1969	7.97	8.55	−0.58	2.10	2.70	−0.60	4.26	4.22	0.04
1970	11.11	9.08	2.03	3.93	2.92	1.01	5.31	4.46	0.85
1971	8.67	9.58	−0.91	2.66	3.12	−0.46	4.40	4.69	−0.29
1972	10.35	10.02	0.33	3.04	3.29	−0.25	5.51	4.90	0.61
1973	10.39	10.36	0.03	3.39	3.42	−0.03	4.86	5.07	−0.21
1974	10.31	10.59	−0.28	3.80	3.51	0.29	4.93	5.20	−0.27
1975	10.47	10.70	−0.23	3.64	3.54	0.10	5.07	5.29	−0.22
1976	13.27	10.70	2.57	4.64	3.53	1.11	6.53	5.32	1.21
1977	11.40	10.60	0.80	3.68	3.47	0.21	5.88	5.32	0.56
1978	10.71	10.43	0.28	3.81	3.37	0.44	5.39	5.29	0.10
1979	9.37	10.22	−0.85	2.99	3.26	−0.27	4.74	5.26	−0.52
1980	10.29	10.03	0.26	2.97	3.13	−0.16	5.41	5.23	0.18
1981	9.74	9.91	−0.17	3.24	3.01	0.23	4.76	5.24	−0.48
1982	11.68	9.94	1.74	3.58	2.93	0.65	6.11	5.32	0.79
1983	11.24	10.19	1.05	3.21	2.90	0.31	6.03	5.50	0.53
1984	10.03	10.75	−0.72	2.73	2.97	−0.24	5.74	5.84	−0.10
1985	10.20	11.73	−1.44	2.15	3.16	−1.01	5.97	6.36	−0.39
1986	13.80	13.25	0.55	3.90	3.51	0.39	7.27	7.14	0.13

(2) Meteorological data

All meteorological data were obtained from the Monthly Weather Record. Braemar was the only station used and therefore provides only an index of climatic change. The climatic variables used were rainfall and temperature between April and August, the heather growing season (see below), September and October rainfall and winter snow lie (days in each month between November and April). Some of these variables may have a delayed effect on the population response and consequently we have considered the influence of the climatic variables up to 24 months prior to the count.

(3) Estimated heather production

Rainfall and temperature in the summer have pronounced effects on the annual primary production of heather[2], an important winter food of deer in the Central and Eastern Highlands[3]. We used climatic data from Braemar to predict the annual production of new heather shoots[4] and then correlated the estimates of stag, hind and total density with the predicted biomass of new heather shoots.

A.3.3   RESULTS

The simple correlations between the polynomial estimates of temporal variation in deer density and changes in the cull, sheep stocks, estimated heather production and selected climatic variables are shown in Table A.3.2. The changes in density since 1961 were correlated positively with summer temperature and negatively with summer rainfall, conditions which influence annual heather production. Densities were high after warm, dry summers but a stronger correlation was obtained with heather production two summers earlier. The temporal variation in deer density was also correlated inversely with changes in sheep numbers but winter conditions seem to have little effect. When both heather production and sheep numbers were included in a multiple regression model both were significant (Table A.3.3). After removing the effects of heather production and sheep numbers, the residual temporal variation in total deer density was negatively correlated to the size of the cull. However, in stags, cull was apparently less important but a

Table A.3.2   Simple correlation coefficients (Pearson's *r*) for relationship between estimated deer density across years using the fit of the polynomial curve (see Appendix 2) with cull, sheep numbers, estimated heather production and climatic variables. Heather production and all climatic variables are for two seasons prior to the count.

	Deer density (per km^2)					
	Total deer		Stags		Hinds	
	r	*p*	*r*	*p*	*r*	*p*
Stag cull (per km^2)	−	−	− 0.123	NS	−	−
Hind cull (per km^2)	−	−	−	−	− 0.230	NS
Adult cull (per km^2)	− 0.112	NS	−	−	−	−
Ewe numbers	− 0.589	**	− 0.800	***	− 0.509	**
Heather production	+ 0.710	***	+ 0.570	**	+ 0.721	***
Summer (April-August) rainfall	− 0.528	**	− 0.439	*	− 0.531	**
Summer temperature	+ 0.634	***	+ 0.507	**	+ 0.646	***
September rainfall	− 0.113	NS	− 0.276	NS	− 0.140	NS
Winter (No. – April) snow lie	− 0.045	NS	− 0.193	NS	+ 0.047	NS
December and January snow lie	− 0.134	NS	− 0.343	+	+ 0.009	NS

NS = Not significant
+ $= 0.1 < p < 0.05$
* $= p < 0.05$
** $= p < 0.01$
*** $= p < 0.001$

significant proportion of the residual variation was explained by snow lie in December and January in the previous winter (Table A.3.3).

A.3.4   DISCUSSION

Temporal variation in both stag and hind density was correlated to the size of sheep stocks in North and West Scotland and estimated heather production. However, the two sexes differed in their response to winter severity and the size of the cull. Stag density, but not hind density, declined following winters with long periods of snow lie. Similar results have been reported within individual populations (see Chapter 5) and also occurred in the analysis of spatial variation in density (see Appendix 4). Surprisingly, hind density but not stag density declined following years when the cull was high. This might suggest that hind culls were relatively more variable between years because the shooting season extends into the winter and stalking depends on the prevailing weather.

Although the model of temporal variation in stag density explained 86% of the variance, the model for hinds only explained

Table A.3.3   Multiple regression models explaining temporal variation (see Table A.3.1) in the polynomial estimates of (a) total deer density (b) stag density (c) hind density. *t*-values and significance levels are after removing effects of the other two variables.

(a) Total deer density explaining 68.2% of the variance.

Variable	Coeff.	t-value	p
Const.	13.34		
Ewes	-9.02 ($\times 10^{-6}$)	-3.95	***
Estimated annual heather production	0.0331	4.60	***
Adult cull	-2.027	-2.46	*

(b) Stag density explaining 86.4% of the variance.

Variable	Coeff.	t-value	
Const.	4.645		
Ewes	-3.52 ($\times 10^{-6}$)	-7.62	***
Estimated annual heather production	0.00885	5.61	***
December & January snow lie	-0.01481	-5.03	***

(c) Hind density explaining 52.0% of the variance.

Variable	Coeff.	t-value	p
Const.	7.84		
Ewes	-3.80 ($\times 10^{-6}$)	-2.85	**
Estimated annual heather production	0.102014	4.63	***
Hind cull	-1.699	-2.39	*

* $= p < 0.05$
** $= p < 0.01$
*** $= p < 0.001$

approximately half the variance. The development of predictive models of the response of deer density to environmental change clearly requires more detailed investigation of the impact of changes in forage quantity and quality, as well as competition with other stock, on deer performance.

REFERENCES

1.   Clutton-Brock, T.H. & Albon, S. D. (1987). *Red Deer in the Highlands: The Ecology of a Marginal Population.* Unpublished report to the Red Deer Commission, Highlands & Islands Development Board and the Rannoch Trust.

2. Miller, G. R. (1979). 'Quantity and quality of the annual production of shrubs and flowers by *Calluna vulgaris* in N.E. Scotland'. *J. Ecology*, **67**, 109–129.

3. Staines, B. W., Crisp, J. & Parish, T. (1982). 'Differences in the quality of food eaten by red deer (*Cervus elaphus*) stags and hinds in winter'. *J. Appl. Ecol.*, **19**, 65–78.

4. Albon, S. D. & Clutton-Brock, T. H. (1988). 'Temporal variation in climate and the population dynamics of red deer in Scotland'. In: *Ecological Change in the Uplands*, ed. M. Usher & D. B. A. Thompson. Blackwell Scientific Publications Ltd., Oxford.

Appendix 4
The Correlates of Spatial
Variation in Deer Density

A.4.1 AIMS

The aims of this analysis were to investigate the environmental factors correlated with the spatial variation in deer density and then develop multiple regression models which predicted the density of deer.

We envisaged three principal applications of models which predicted the density of deer.

(1) to estimate the number of deer occupying ground not previously covered by the Red Deer Commission's census;
(2) to indicate which areas carry unusually high or low deer populations on the basis of their topography, soils, climate and utilisation by man;
(3) to provide some indication of the likely effects on density of major changes in management policy, especially of changes in culling policy and sheep numbers.

A.4.2 MATERIALS AND METHODS

(1) The spatial unit: the parish

Although variation in deer density between the Commission's blocks was approximately three times greater than the within-block variation (between parishes), the latter was significant (see Appendix 2). Consequently the analysis of spatial variation in deer density was carried out at the parish level. This proved a suitable unit area because estate boundaries frequently match with those of parishes, so estate deer records were grouped easily into parishes and also, the agricultural statistics returned to the Department of Agriculture and Fisheries for Scotland (DAFS) were collated into parish units.

The analysis focused on the 48 parishes within the Highland

Table A.4.1 Estimated densities of deer in different parishes within the Highland Region (excluding Skye), standardized for 1986.

	Density (numbers per km^2)				Density (numbers per km^2)		
	Total deer (incl. calves)	Stags	Hinds		Total deer (incl. calves)	Stags	Hinds
Farr	11.1	2.7	6.5	Kilmorach	19.3	6.2	9.7
Latheron	17.9	3.6	10.6	Kiltarlity	12.1	4.7	5.6
Halkirk	5.6	0.8	3.5	Urquhart	6.0	1.7	3.8
Reay	6.6	1.0	4.0	Urray	17.4	4.5	9.4
Kildonan	13.6	4.5	6.7	Glenshiel	18.8	6.1	9.3
Lochbroom	7.7	2.6	4.8	Kintail	19.6	5.2	10.6
Assynt	8.4	2.3	4.5	Lochalsh	18.3	4.3	10.3
Creich	5.5	1.8	4.3	Arisaig & Moidart	14.0	4.3	7.0
Eddrachilles	4.5	3.4	1.4	Glenelg	17.3	5.8	8.3
Lairg	6.4	2.0	5.0	Kilmallie	13.5	3.8	7.0
Golspie	12.0	2.9	6.7	Kilmonvaig	13.6	4.8	6.4
Rogart	8.8	2.7	4.5	Ardnamurchan	7.0	2.1	3.8
Clyne	11.7	2.6	6.7	Ardgour	10.7	2.9	5.7
Loth	7.0	2.9	3.1	Morvern	13.6	3.2	7.7
Gairloch	6.8	1.9	4.1	Boleskine & Abertaff	15.2	3.4	8.6
Contin	15.6	4.4	8.5	Alvie	17.3	5.3	8.8
Alness	13.5	2.7	8.1	Duthill & Rothiemurchus	15.2	3.0	8.8
Fodderty	13.4	4.0	6.8	Kingussie & Insh	19.5	4.6	3.7
Kiltearn	17.0	4.3	9.3	Laggan	20.1	5.3	10.9
Rossheen	6.3	2.1	2.9	Daviot & Dunlichty	17.8	8.7	6.6
Edderton	3.3	1.0	1.6	Moy & Dalarossie	13.1	4.0	6.7
Kincardine	9.4	2.9	7.7	Abernethy & Kincardine	8.0	2.4	4.3
Applecross	6.0	1.8	4.1	Lismore & Appin	10.1	1.8	5.9
Lochcarron	7.6	2.7	4.3	Rhum	20.7	7.1	9.8

Region since systematic environmental data were not available outside this region.

(2) The calculation of density and cull rates

Since some parishes did not fall entirely within the Commission's count blocks it was necessary to calculate a weighted average density using the two or three estimates from different parts of the same parish. For example, the parish of Kildonan, Sutherland, was split between Blocks 1, 2, and 4, so we calculated an average density weighted by the area of each part. The part of Kildonan in Block 4 had the largest area and therefore the weighted average reflected the density here more closely than the parts in Blocks 1 and 2.

The parish of Kildonan also provides an example of the correction needed for estimates for blocks covered only once. The part of Kildonan in Block 1 had only one deer count which needed correcting to the standardised year (1986). This was done by multiplying the counted density by the ratio of the mean density in 1986 over the mean density in the year Block 1 was counted. The parish values used in the analysis are given in Table A.4.1.

Although stag and hind density were positively correlated across parishes in the Highland Region ($r = 0.5895$, $p < 0.001$) we have analysed the two sexes separately because differences in their breeding biology mean they respond to environmental variability in different ways (Chapters 4, 5 and 6).

(3) Environmental variables

Our analysis considered four main groups of variables that seemed likely to affect the density or performance of deer either directly or indirectly.

(1) *Soil types* with associated vegetation communities.
(2) *Topographical variables* including altitude, aspect and stream length.
(3) *Climatic variables*, including average minimum January temperature, July sunshine (hours per day).
(4) *Human settlement and management variables*, including the number of settlements, road length, details of deer culled, the number of sheep kept in the parish.

Table A.4.2   The environmental variables used in the multiple regression models of spatial variation in deer densities within the Highland Region.

Soil type.	*Vegetation communities[4,5,6].*
1. Brown forest soils.	Acid Bent-Fescue grassland.
2. Brown forest soils, humus iron podzols.	Acid Bent grassland, dry Atlantic heather moor.
3. Humus iron podzols.	Arable and permanent pastures, Bent-Fescue grassland.
4. Peaty podzols, humus iron podzols.	Atlantic and Boreal heather moor, bog, heather moor.
5. Peaty podzols, peaty gleys, peat, peaty rankers.	Atlantic and Boreal heather moor, blanket and flying-Bent bog.
6. Peaty podzols, peat, peaty gleys.	Moist Atlantic heather moor, blanket bog.
7. Non-calcareous gleys, humic gleys.	Arable and permanent pastures, rush pastures and sedge mires.
8. Non-calcareous gleys, peaty gleys.	Permanent pastures, bog heather moor and blanket bog.
9. Peaty gleys, peat.	Bog heather moor.
10. Peaty gleys, peaty podzols, peaty rankers.	Bog and northern bog, heather moor.
11. Subalpine soils.	Mountain heath, upland Bent-Fescue grasslands.
12. Subalpine soils, peat.	Mountain heath, mountain blanket bog.
13. Alpine soils, subalpine soils.	Mountain heath communities, stiff sedge-Fescue grassland.
14. Alpine soils.	Alpine lichen heath, Fescue fringe-moss heath.
15. Rankers, peaty podzols.	Dry Atlantic and Boreal heather moor.
16. Peat.	Blanket and flying-Bent bog.
17. Alluvial soils.	Arable and permanent pastures, rush pastures and sedge mires.
18. Bare rock, scree.	Lichen.
19. Rankers and lithosols.	Blaeberry and bog whortleberry heath.

Topographical variables. The proportion of each kilometre square in the four altitude classes 20–23.

20. Altitude <76 metres.
21. Altitude 77–198 metres.
22. Altitude 199–488 metres.
23. Altitude 489–1344 metres.
24. Minimum elevation (metres).
25. Maximum elevation (metres).

26. Height of hill behind (metres).
27. Distance to hill behind.
28. Aspect (degrees from North).
29. Number of lochs.
30. Length of single line stream.
31. Length of double line stream.
32. Length of coastline.

Climatic variables.

33. Average number of days snowfall per year.
34. Average minimum January temperature.
35. Average daily hours of sunshine for July.
36. Accumulated temperature: day-degrees Celsius greater than 5.6°C, approximately the level at which plant growth commences.

Table A.4.2 *(continued)*

37. Potential water deficit: the excess of potential evaporation/transpiration over rainfall.
38. Exposure: based on the wind effect (speed together with temperature, relative humidity and salt content near coasts) on broad-leaved trees growing singly, and on common heather, *Calluna vulgaris*.
39. Accumulated frost: day-degrees Celsius less than 0°C accumulated over the period of one year.

Human settlement.

40. Frequency of woods.
41. Number of settlements.
42. Length of main road (A class).
43. Length of metalled road>4m width.
44. Length of fenced minor road.
45. Length of unfenced minor road.
46. Presence of footpath.

Domestic stock.

47. Sheep density: the natural logarithm of the expression (sheep density + 25) where the density of all sheep, excluding lambs, is expressed per km² of rough grazing in order to normalise the skewed distribution.
48. Cattle density: the natural logarithm of the density of hill cattle per km².

Deer management.

49. Stag cull: the natural logarithm of the expression (proportion culled + 0.15) in order to normalise the skewed distribution.
50. Hind cull: the natural logarithm of the expression (proportion culled + 0.05).
51. Number of full-time stalkers.
52. Number of part-time stalkers and ghillies.

We obtained measures of topography, climate and settlement for each of 27,915 1 km² grid squares covering the Highland Region, Scotland (Figure 2.1) which had been compiled from Ordnance Survey 1:50,000 maps and Meteorological Office maps by the Highland Regional Council[1]. To this dataset we added additional climatic variables, including accumulated temperature and potential water deficit, and measures of exposure[2,3], as well as information on soils taken from maps produced by the Macaulay Institute for Soil Research[4,5,6].

Unfortunately, systematic information on the relative abundance of different vegetation types is not available for most Highland parishes. However, there is a reasonably close relationship between soil and sward types and the abundance of different soils provides an indicator of the availability of the principal vegetation communities (see Table A.4.2).

Each 1 km² grid square was then assigned to a parish if more than 50% of its area was within the parish. The mean of each variable was calculated across all the squares in the parish to give a single value for each parish. The minimum value of Minimum elevation and maximum value of Maximum elevation were used.

We also obtained information on the density of sheep and cattle in each parish from the agricultural returns made to the Department of Agriculture and Fisheries for Scotland (DAFS) at the June census. A complete list of the 52 variables used in the analysis is given in Table A.4.2.

A.4.3   ANALYSIS

The analysis begins by investigating the simple correlations between our dependent variables (deer density, stag density, etc.) and each of the 52 independent variables. However, unless these correlations are very high, we are unlikely to obtain a good predictive equation from the simple linear regression of density on a single independent variable. Two or more independent variables may give additional information about density by means of multiple regression. In our case, using all 52 variables would be unwieldy and we have attempted to find a predictive equation based on the best half dozen variables.

We used the multiple regression routine in the GENSTAT statistical package[7]. Initially we entered the variables in a stepwise procedure. The first independent variable to be included is the one with the highest correlation coefficient. Having fitted the regression line the residuals are calculated and in turn regressed on the other 51 variables. Again the variable with the highest correlation is included, the new residuals are calculated and in turn regressed on the other 50 variables, and so on, giving an equation of the form

$$y = b_0 + b_1 x_1 + b_2 x_2 + \ldots \ldots + b_N x_N$$

At each stage we tested whether the addition of the extra variable significantly reduced the residual sums of squares. However, because many of the variables were inter-correlated, the inclusion of some of the variables in later steps occasionally resulted in one of the early variables no longer being significant. In this case the non-significant variable was dropped from the model and the stepwise procedure continued as described above. In the final model each variable explained a significant amount of the residual variation having controlled for all the other variables included in the model, as if it was added to the multiple regression in the last step.

Multiple regression has its own problems. In particular, where two variables are closely inter-correlated, it may be unable to distinguish between their effects. Where stepwise techniques are used, this may mean that the effects of two independent but inter-correlated variables may be attributed to the first one included in the model. For example, if altitude and soil type are both closely correlated with deer density, the removal of the statistical effects of altitude may leave no significant relationship between the residual variation and soil type even if both altitude and soil type exert independent influences on deer density. When interpreting multiple regression analyses, it is consequently important to be aware of the extent to which the independent variables are inter-related.

A.4.4 RESULTS

(1) Simple correlations between deer density and environmental variables

Topography

Stag density was positively, and significantly, correlated with height of hill behind, the proportion of ground over 488 metres, the maximum elevation of the ground and with the increasing southerly and westerly aspect of the parish (see Table A.4.3). Stag density was correlated negatively with the proportion of ground under 198 metres.

Hind density and total deer density (including calves) showed similar correlations with most of the topographical variables, but was not significantly correlated with aspect and showed a significant negative relationship with the number of lochs (see Table A.4.3). In general, correlations between hind density and topographical variables were weaker than between stag density and the same variables, suggesting that stag numbers may be more strongly affected by topography than those of hinds.

Since all the altitude measures used were highly inter-correlated, interpretation of simple correlations was difficult (see Section A.4.3). For example, aspect was positively correlated with Maximum elevation ($r = 0.4139$, $p < 0.01$) and negatively correlated with Altitude $77-198$ m ($r = -0.3197$, $p < 0.05$).

Table A.4.3   Bivariate correlations between deer density and environmental variables across 48 parishes in the Highland Region.

Topography

Positive correlations:	Stag density			Hind density			Total deer density (incl. calves)	
	r	p		r	p			
Height of hill behind	0.5334	****		0.4481	**		0.5280	***
Altitude>488m	0.4600	**		0.3876	**		0.4457	**
Maximum elevation	0.3659	*		0.4229	**		0.4536	**
Aspect	0.3828	**		0.0997	NS		0.2359	NS
Negative correlations:								
Altitude<76m	−0.4108	**		−0.3425	*		−0.4064	**
Altitude 77−198m	−0.4981	***		−0.3023	*		−0.4094	**
Number of lochs	−0.2412	NS		−0.3049	*		−0.2974	*

Soils

Positive correlations:	Stag density			Hind density			Total deer density	
	r	p		r	p			
Subalpine soils	0.6190	***		0.4811	***		0.5895	***
Peaty gleys, peat and peaty podzols, peaty rankers	0.2972	*		0.1595	NS		0.2405	NS
Negative correlations:								
Alpine and subalpine soils	−0.3087	*		−0.2994	*		−0.3180	*

Climate

Positive correlations:	Stag density			Hind density			Total deer density	
	r	p		r	p			
Frost	0.3788	**		0.3180	*		0.3662	*
Negative correlations: Potential water deficit	−0.3027	*		−0.2836	NS		−0.3386	*

Human activities

Positive correlations:	Stag density			Hind density			Total deer density	
	r	p		r	p			
Number of full-time stalkers	0.2591	NS		0.4498	**			
Total number of stalkers/ghilles	0.2948	*		0.3595	*			
Negative correlations: proportion culled	−0.5823	***		−0.2239	NS		−0.2664	NS

Soils

The distribution of subalpine soil was the best predictor of density for both sexes and total deer density. Stag density was positively related to the area of subalpine soils (soil type 11, Table A.4.2), as well as to peaty gleys (Table A.4.3). Hind density and total deer density were positively related to the area of subalpine soils (soil type 11, Table A.4.2) but were unrelated to the area of peaty gleys. Stag, hind and total deer density were all negatively related to the area of alpine and subalpine soils (soil type 13, Table A.4.2).

The distribution of subalpine soils was correlated strongly with several of the altitude variables, including height of hill behind ($r = 0.6416$, $p < 0.001$), maximum elevation ($r = 0.5724$, $p < 0.001$), altitude > 488 m ($r = 0.4538$, $p < 0.01$), altitude $77 - 198$ m ($r = 0.4755$, $p < 0.001$) and aspect ($r = 0.3362$, $p < 0.05$).

Climate

Stag, hind and total deer density were positively correlated with measures of accumulated frost and negatively correlated with potential water deficit (Table A.4.3). It seemed likely that these relationships were caused by inter-correlation between climate and other environmental variables, particularly altitude.

Human activity

Both stag and hind density were positively related to the density of stalkers and ghillies employed in the parishes, while stag, but not hind density or total deer density, was significantly, negatively correlated with the proportion of animals culled (Table A.4.3). Neither stag nor hind density was significantly correlated with sheep numbers.

(2)   Multiple regression models of deer density in Highland Region

Total deer density

Total deer density was related positively to the proportion of peaty

Table A.4.4　　Multiple regression model of (a) total deer density (b) stag density and (c) hind density across 48 parishes in the Highland Region using the environmental variables shown in Table A.4.2. Values of *t*-test are for relationships having fitted all the other variables.

(a) *Total deer density*

		Coeff.	t-test	p
	Constant	4.43		
Environmental variable				
Topographical:	Altitude>488m	0.2576	3.05	**
	Number of lochs	− 4.9900	4.30	***
Soils:	Subalpine soils	0.1471	2.84	**
	Non-calcareous gleys	0.4520	2.58	*
	Peaty podzols	0.1518	3.34	**
Human	Log_e (sheep density + 25)	− 5.51	3.56	***
activity	Log_e (proportion adults culled + 0.10)	− 15.06	4.54	***

(b) *Stag density*

		Coeff.	t-test	p
	Constant	4.13		
Environmental variable				
Topographical:	Altitude < 76m	− 0.3136	− 3.80	***
	Stream length	− 0.0534	− 2.02	*
Soils:	Subalpine soils	0.1070	5.66	***
	Non-calcareous gleys	0.1889	2.81	**
	Peat and peaty podzols	− 0.0229	− 2.51	*
Climate:	Days snow fall	− 0.0390	− 2.53	*
Human activity:	Log_e (proportion culled + 0.15)	− 2.9690	− 5.55	***

(c) *Hind density*

		Coeff.	t-test	p
	Constant	12.46		
Environmental variable				
Topographical:	Altitude < 76m	− 0.961	− 5.22	***
	Altitude 199 − 488m	− 0.2274	− 2.78	*
Soils:	Subalpine soils	0.1231	4.14	***
	Brown Forest soils	0.3498	3.72	***
Human activity:	Log_e (proportion culled + 0.05)	− 1.796	− 3.34	**
	Log_e (sheep density + 25)	− 2.404	− 2.62	*
	Number settlements	2.969	4.32	***

podzols, non-calcareous gleys, subalpine soils and altitude above 488 metres. Not surprisingly the last two were significantly, positively inter-correlated. However, the most significant relationships were all negative ones, including the mean number of lochs per km^2, the density of sheep and the proportion of adults culled (see Table A.4.4).

Although it might seem surprising that high deer densities occur at high altitudes and on subalpine soils, these habitats commonly support preferred mountain heaths and upland Bent-Fescue grasslands. Similarly, peaty podzols are characterised by Bent-bog and heather moor communities while non-calcareous gleys are typified by permanent pasture and arable. The negative association with sheep density might reflect competition for these preferred vegetation communities (see Chapter 4). However, it would appear that the proportion culled is having the greatest effect on deer density in the Highland Region.

Stag density

Stag density was positively related to the area of subalpine soils and non-calcareous gleys and negatively to the area of ground under 76 metres, stream length, the area of peat and peaty podzols, average number of days of snow fall and the proportion culled.

Stag numbers were high in parishes where subalpine soils (which commonly support swards dominated by bents, fescues and herbs) and non-calcareous gleys (which are typically associated with swards dominated by broad-leaved grasses and preferred by stags (see Chapter 4)) were abundant. Long periods of snow lie and high culling rates can both reduce stag density.

Hind density

Hind density was positively related to the area of subalpine soils, Brown Forest soils and to the number of human settlements, and negatively to the area of ground under 76 metres and intermediate altitudes between 199–488 metres, to sheep density and to the proportion culled.

The major difference between this model and the one for stags is the importance of the Brown Forest soils, which typically support acid Bent-Fescue grassland, and the presence of human habitation. While it is well established that hinds select swards dominated by narrow-leaved grasses (see Chapter 4) we do not understand the positive association with number of settlements.

Although there were five significant inter-correlations between the seven variables included in the model of hind density, only the negative correlation between the distribution of Brown Forest soils and altitude 199−488 metres ($r = -0.2906$, $p < 0.05$) cause concern about the spurious inclusion of the proportion of ground at intermediate altitudes.

(3)   Evaluation of multiple regression models of deer density

The models of stag and total deer density both account for an appreciable portion of inter-parish variation (72% and 61% respectively) though, in the case of hinds (52% of variance explained), a substantial proportion of the variation is still unexplained. The majority of the relationships revealed appear likely to have a causal basis, on grounds of common sense and our knowledge of the ecology of particular deer populations. Similarly, the differences between the factors affecting hind and stag densities coincide closely with our understanding of the ecology of the two sexes. For example, the negative relationship between sheep density and hind density, but not stag density, might reflect the greater overlap in habitat use between sheep and hinds (see Chapter 4), while the influence of prolonged snow lie on stag density, but not hind density, may occur because stags enter the winter in poorer condition than hinds and are more likely to die in severe winter weather (see Chapter 5, Appendix 3).

It seems unlikely that any misclassification of animals in the Commission's counts (see Chapter 2) had a major influence on these relationships since the extent of misclassification was small relative to the ten-fold range of densities between parishes. Nevertheless, it might strengthen some relationships and weaken others.

A.4.5   APPLICATIONS OF MODELS OF DEER DENSITY

(1)   Estimation of deer density

Given the environmental information used in the models described in Table A.4.4, it should be possible to estimate the total number of deer, stags and hinds an area of ground might carry. However, even though the estimates are approximate, and their confidence limits are broad, it provides the first non-arbitrary way of estimating the likely density of deer.

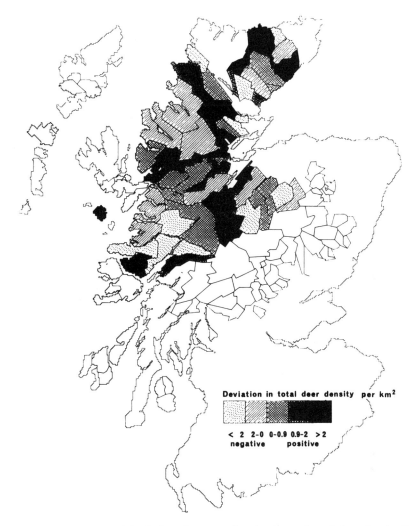

Figure A.4.1   Map of deviations from predicted values of total deer density for parishes within the Highland Region, excluding Skye (shaded parishes). Open parishes are outside the Highland Region or have not yet been counted by the Red Deer Commission.

Future counts, for example, the larger part of North Sutherland, which has not been covered, will enable us to evaluate how useful the model is in estimating deer density.

(2)   Measurement of relative densities

We suspect the main use of the models is to identify parishes which carry unusually high or unusually low densities of stags and hinds. For example, Figure A.4.1 shows the deviations of the observed total deer densities in the 48 parishes in the Highland region from the expected values generated from the multiple regression model in Table A.4.4a.

Investigating the fit of the models in this way has two potential uses. First, in some cases there will be sound ecological reasons for unusually high, or unusually low, densities. These deviations may help to indicate important environmental variables that have been omitted from the model, whose inclusion might increase its predictive value. Second, they may help to identify parishes that are either over- or under-stocked.

(3)   The probable effects of management changes

Another use of the model could be to estimate the likely effects of management changes. For example, average hind density declined by 1 per km^2 for a doubling in sheep density from 25 to 50 per km^2, while stag density did not appear to be affected. Similarly, hind and stag density declined by 0.33 per km^2 and 0.54 per km^2, respectively as the cull increased from 10% to 15%.

It should be emphasised that these estimates are only approximate. Analysis of temporal changes in density following major changes in management within parishes would provide a more reliable basis for estimating the effects of changes in sheep density or culling policy.

REFERENCES

1.   Bunce, R. G. H., Claridge, C., Barr, C. J. & Baldwin, M. B. (1984). 'The use of simple data in the production of strategic sampling systems – its application to the Highland Region, Scotland'. In: *Proceedings of First International Seminar on Methodology in Ecological Research and Planning*.

2.   Birse, E. L. & Dry, F.T. (1970). *Assessment of Climatic Conditions in Scotland 1. Based on Accumulated Temperature and Potential Water Deficit*. Macaulay Institute for Soil Research, Aberdeen.

3.   Birse, E. L. & Robertson, L (1970). *Assessment of Climatic Conditions in Scotland 2. Based on Exposure and Accumulated Frost*. Macaulay Institute for Soil Research, Aberdeen.

4. Futty, D. W. & Towers, W. (1982). *Soil and Land Capability for Agriculture. Northern Scotland*. Macaulay Institute for Soil Research, Aberdeen.

5. Bibby, J. S., Hudson, G. & Henderson, D. J. (1982). *Soil and Land Capability for Agriculture. Western Scotland*. Macaulay Institute for Soil Research, Aberdeen.

6. Walker, A. D., Campbell, G. G. B., Heslop, R. E. F., Gauld, J. H., Laing, D., Shipley, B. M. & Wright, G. G. (1982). *Soil and Land Capability for Agriculture. Eastern Scotland*. Macaulay Institute for Soil Research, Aberdeen.

7. Alvey, N., Galway, N. & Lane, P. (1982). *An Introduction to Genstat*. Academic Press, London.

Appendix 5
Deer Densities in the Red Deer Commission's Counting Blocks

The following table shows the density of deer (numbers per km^2) in the last count across the Red Deer Commission's counting blocks: (1) total deer (including calves); (2) stag density; (3) hind density; (4) the number of calves per 100 hinds.

	Area (km^2)	Year	Total deer (1)	Density in last RDC count		Calves per 100 hinds (4)
				Stag (2)	Hind (3)	
1. N. Sutherland	419*	1985	3.3	1.1	1.7	28.3
2. Caithness/Sutherland	223	1986	17.4	3.5	10.4	33.5
3. W. Sutherland	696	1986	6.3	1.9	3.3	35.6
	228	1981	3.3	1.1	1.4	57.6
4. E. Sutherland	623	1976	5.9	2.0	2.9	35.2
5. Wester Ross	998	1979	8.1	2.5	4.2	32.5
	227	1975	9.7	2.8	5.0	38.4
6. North Ross	769	1975	7.8	2.8	3.7	34.6
	1258	1984	8.4	1.8	5.1	27.9
7. Rovie/Skibo			No data			
8. Gairloch Cons. Unit	371	1981	3.2	0.9	1.6	47.4
9. Applecross	226	1965	4.7	0.9	2.6	44.0
10. Shieldaig/Ledgowan	311	1974	5.5	2.8	1.8	45.5
11. South Ross	1680	1984	13.9	4.1	7.7	28.0
12. Glenmoriston/Glenurquhart	217	1974	4.5	1.7	1.9	48.6
13. W. Inverness	184	1985	10.8	3.2	5.5	38.7
	1199	1985	12.5	3.5	6.5	37.7

	Block						
14.	Ardochy/Port Clair	122	1974	4.1	1.6	1.6	51.3
15.	W. Loch Shiel	183	1983	9.6	3.0	5.1	30.9
16.	Ardnamurchan	156	1983	5.1	1.9	2.3	40.6
17.	Conaglen/Ardgour	285	1986	8.9	2.0	4.9	40.5
18.	Morvern	306	1986	13.0	3.4	6.6	45.1
19.	Monadhliaths	1505	1977	13.4	4.6	6.6	33.3
20.	Cabrach/Glen Fiddich	355	1967	0.9	0.2	0.6	32.0
21.	Cairngorm/W. Grampians	468	1983	6.8	1.5	4.1	30.4
		1751	1983	17.0	5.7	8.6	31.9
22.	Ben Nevis/Blackmount	799	1982	9.4	2.5	5.0	37.7
		373	1978	7.4	2.7	3.6	31.4
23.	Corrour/Ben Alder/Ardverikie	456	1986	19.8	5.4	10.6	36.4
24.	E. Loch Ericht	325	1985	14.9	3.7	8.2	35.8
25.	E. Grampians	1274	1986	19.7	5.8	10.6	31.6
26.	Rannoch/S. Tay	877	1979	8.1	2.7	4.1	31.0
27.	S. Loch Tay	495	1986	7.2	1.5	4.2	35.3
28.	Argyll	318*	1980	5.6	1.2	3.2	35.5
29.	Trossachs	256*	1981	2.4	0.5	1.4	34.1
30.	Glenartney	146	1986	34.3	10.0	18.0	35.3
31.	Galloway			No data			
32.	Harris/Lewis	566	1982	6.3	1.2	3.6	42.4
33.	N. Uist	310	1985	1.4	0.4	0.7	43.3
34.	Skye	449	1980	1.9	0.4	1.1	40.7
35.	Scalpay			No data			
36.	Rhum	87	1986	19.8	6.7	9.5	38.6
37.	Mull	194	1979	2.2	0.7	1.0	43.1
		172	1979	5.6	1.4	3.1	36.3
		113	1986	6.7	1.9	3.3	45.9
38.	Scarba			No data			
39.	Jura	318	1978	18.5	6.9	8.8	32.4
40.	Islay	130*	1975	9.9	2.8	4.7	49.9
41.	Arran	148	1981	14.3	5.2	6.8	33.4

*Only part of Block counted.

Subject Index

age
  birth weights, 65, 67
  calf condition, 65
  calf mortality, 65, 67
  effect on autumn weight, 65
  effect on condtion, 65
  effect on fighting success, 65
  estimation, 64
  mortality rate, 64, 67
  reproductive success, 63–7, 70
Agriculture (Scotland) Act (1948), 17
Agrostis/Festuca grassland, 88, 81,
  99, 100, 146
Agrostis spp., 80, 85, 88, 93, 103
alder, browsing susceptibility, 167
Aldourie, 173
Alnus glutinosa, see alder
altitude
  effect on hind weight, 62
  effect on population density, 33
  seasonal ranging, 93
antler growth
  effect of culling, 71, 199
  effect of density, 123, 124, 125,
    126, 187, 189
antler shedding, effect of snow, 137,
  138
appetite, 83
  seasonal variation, 83–5
Applecross, 32
Ardochy, 32
Ardtornish, habitat use, 79
Ardverikie, 29
Arran, 30
ash, 171
aspen, 171, 191
  browsing susceptibility, 167
Atholl, 14 15
avian tuberculosis, 101

bark stripping, 169
beech, 171
  bark stripping, 169
Ben Alder, 29
bents, see *Agrostis* spp.
Betula. spp., see birch
bilberry, see blaeberry
birch, browsing susceptibility, 167
birth date, 55

calf mortality, 177, 185
  climate, 140–41
birth weight, 68, 70
  calf mortality, 56, 124, 150, 186
  climate, 141, 142, 149, 187
  density, 123, 124, 186
  effect of mother's age, 65, 67
  effect of mother's dominance rank,
    55
  effect of temperature, 141, 142, 187
  in milk and yeld hinds, 68, 70
  subsequent reproductive success,
    147
Black Mount, 14, 15
blaeberry, 79, 87, 173
  browsing susceptibility, 171
block-year model, 25–6, 216–26
body size
  diet differences between sexes,
    93–4, 188
  effect of habitat, 2, 13, 161
body temperature, effect on
  digestibility, 90
bog cotton, 79, 87, 96, 103
Braemar, 93, 133, 144, 147, 148, 229
browsing damage to trees, 167

cattle
  deer, 101–102
  sheep, 102
Calluna vulgaris, *see* heather
Capreolus capreolus, *see* roe deer
carrying capacity
  ecological, 202, 203
  economic, 202
Cervidae, evolution and distribution,
  11–13
Cervus spp.
  antler evolution, 13
  appearance, 13
  world distribution, 9
Cervus canadensis, *see* wapiti
Cervus nippon, *see* sika deer
Chinese water deer, 11
clegs, 91
climate, 133–56, *see also* snow,
    rainfall, temperature and weather
  adult mortality, 147–9
  birth weight, 141, 142, 149, 187

body weight, 135−9
calf mortality 143−7
   conception date, 140−41
   effect on birth date, 140−41
   energy requirements, 133
   fecundity, 139−40, 187
   food availability & quality, 135
   management, 152−3
   population stability, 191−2
climatic correlates of survival and
      reproduction, 134−5
cohort
   culling, 153
   of mother and calf mortality, 15,
      187
   significance for reproductive
      success, 149−52, 187
competition
   between sexes, 93, 94, 188
   with roe deer, 173
   with sheep, 99
   with sika deer, 173
Conaglen/Ardgour, 31
conception date
   effect on calf mortality, 117, 185
   in commercial forests, 162, 163
   effect of density, 117, 119
   effect of weather, 140−41
   synchrony, 51−3, 54
   yeld and milk hinds, 67−8
conception threshold weight, 116,
      161, 185
condition
   effect of age, 65
   kidney fat index, 65, 69
   rump fat index, 69
   of yeld hinds, 67, 69
Corrour, 29
counts, 23−9
   accuracy 25, 195, 210−15
   block-year model, 25−6
   difficulties, 25
   in forests, 159
   historical, 16
   importance for max. sustainable
      yield estimation, 128
   improvements for management, 40
   by Nature Conservancy (Council),
      16, 26, 210, 211
   by Red Deer Commission, 2, 17,
      26, 210
   R.D.C. counting blocks, 23, 217
   R.D.C. counting methods, 23−4

   standardisation of block counts, 25
counting blocks, 23, 217
   deer density in, 248−9
   frequency of counts in, 217
culling level
   averages, 15, 16, 193
   current total, 8, 34, 35
   density of, 27
   geographical variation, 37, 38, 39
   required in commercial forests, 163
   temporal changes, 36
culling, 34−7, 193−200
   effect on antler form, 71, 199
   effect on density, 29, 33
   effect on reproductive success,
      199−200
   importance of count accuracy, 195
   importance of hind density, 70−71
   income, 8
   justifications, 202−205
   male dispersal, 72
   natural mortality, 152, 197−9
   of older hinds, 70, 199
   population stability, 190−91
   problems caused by forests, 176−7
   recruitment, 37, 194, 196
   of specific cohorts, 153
   of yeld hinds, 70
culling model, 196−7
culling, necessary research, 193−200
   effect on population density,
      195−7
   level for population control, 193−5
   reproductive performance,
      199−200

day-length
   appetite, 83
   timing of rut, 54
Deer (Scotland) Act (1959), 16
deer fences, 159
   effect on hill populations, 171
deer sedge, 79, 87, 91, 96, 99, 103
deforestation in Scotland, 14
density, 23−34, 113−31
   adult sex ratio, 187
   age of sexual maturity, 115, 185
   antler growth, 123, 124, 125, 126,
      187, 189
   birth weight, 123, 124, 186
   conception threshold weight, 116,
      161, 185
   conception date, 117, 119

correlates of spatial variation,
    233–47
culling, 29, 33, 38, 70–71
dispersal, 124–5, 186
drainage, 33
effect of altitude, 33
effect on fecundity, 67, 115–18,
    161, 185
effect of forestry, 38, 102, 103
effect of sheep, 29, 33, 38,
    100–101
effect on tree regeneration, 96, 104
estimation in forests, 159–60
food limitation 190
growth, 124
habitat use, 188
intersexual effects, 113
limitation by food, 190
research questions, 189–90
soil type, 33
density and management, 37–40
    determination of optimal density,
        125–8
density models
    applications, 244–6
    block-year model, 216–26
    estimates of deer density 227–8
    estimates of heather production,
        229
    parish-year model, 219
    temporal variation, 228–32
density and mortality
    adult, 120
    calf, summer, 117, 119, 120
    calf, winter, 119, 121, 124, 185
    climate, 147
    neonatal, 119, 186
    sex differences, 119, 121, 187
density variation
    of averages, 25, 26, 185
    correlates of spatial variation,
        233–47
    geographical, 29–34, 248–9
    methods of investigation,
        113–15
    temporal, 28, 29
    topography, 239–40
Department of Agriculture and
    Fisheries (Scotland) (DAFS), 233,
    238
    sheep censuses, 8
Deschampsia spp., 88
Deschampsia flexuosa, 85, 171

diet
    availability of live food, 80
    comparison with sheep, 99–101
    comparison with roe deer, 164, 173
    comparison with sika deer, 173
    composition, 85–7
    in forests, 167
    milk / yeld hind differences, 94
    sex differences, 93–4, 188
    trace mineral balance, 80
diet preferences, 87–92, 102
    effects of weather, 92
    variation between individuals, 92
    nitrogen content, 89
digestibility of vegetation, 79, 80, 89
    effect of body temperature, 90
    selection by the sexes, 93–4
digestion, 99
dispersal
    in commercial forests, 166, 174
    culling, 72
    effect of density, 124–5, 186
    of hinds, 48, 49
    research questions, 189–90
    of stags, 47, 48, 71–2
Douglas fir, bark stripping, 169
drainage, effect on deer density, 33
Dundonnell, 64

ecological studies of red deer, 2–7
elk, N. American, 125, 147, 169, 191
energy consumption of deer and
    sheep, 99
Eriophorum vaginatum, see bog
    cotton

Fagus sylvatica, see beech
fecundity
    age of sexual maturity, 115, 185
    age-specific, 63, 65, 67
    in commercial forests, 161, 162,
        163, 166, 167
    effect of body weight, 116–7, 118
    effect of climate, 139–40, 187
    effect of food availability, 116
    effect of matrilineal group size, 186
    of milk/yeld hinds, 67
    population density 115–18, 161
feeding, diurnal pattern, 83
fescues, see Festuca spp.
Festuca spp., 80, 85, 88, 93, 94, 103
feeding competition
    between sexes, 93–4, 167

fighting success, 50
  age, 65
  in rut, 50
forestry, commercial, 38, 102, 103,
    159–83
  effects on red deer populations,
      174–7, 193
  extent in Scotland, 159
forestry, deer damage prevention,
    171, 174
  culling rate, 163
  culling difficulties, 176–7
  fencing, 171
  plantation design, 174, 193
forest red deer, 159–83
  activity patterns, 166
  bark stripping, 169–70
  body size, 161
  browsing damage, 167–8
  calf mortality, 163
  conception date, 162, 163
  deer density and damage, 125
  deer densities, 159–61, 164
  diet, 167
  dispersal, 166, 174
  fecundity, 161, 162, 163, 166, 167
  foetal sex ratio, 163
  habitat use, 164–7, 173
  home range, 166
  impact on forests, 167–71
  spread of sika deer, 177, 173–4
  twinning, 161–3
  vulnerability of tree species to
      damage, 167–70

Gairloch, 32
gestation, cost of, 67
Glenartney, 14, 15, 29
Glenbranter, 159, 163, 174
  forest habitat use, 164–5
  roe deer, 164, 173
Glen Cripesdale, 159
Glen Dye, 93, 115, 117
  habitat use, 79
Glenfeshie, 185
  altitude and terrain, 5
  conception date distribution, 54
  climate, 133, 134
    birth weight, 142
    calving date, 140
    fecundity, 140
    hind weight, 139
    mortality, 143, 147–8

density, 5
  changes, 115
  fecundity, 116–17
diet and habitat use, 79
fecundity of yeld hinds, 67
growing season, 81
R.D.C. counts, 23
supplementary feeding, 98
tree regeneration and grazing, 96
weight
  larder weights, 137, 160
  of mother and calf condition, 65,
      67
  winter temperatures and body
      weights, 61, 138
winter home ranges, 93
Glen Fiddich, 15, 32, 145
Glen Goibhre, habitat use, 79
Glenmoriston, 32
Glenurquhart, 32
golden eagle, 201
grass growth, 80
  effect of rainfall, 81–2
  effect of temperature, 80–81
  live standing crop (September), 82
grazing, 94–6
  effect of cattle, 101
  management, 94
  relative importance of sheep and
      deer, 95
  species composition, 94, 95
  tree regeneration, 96, 104, 169
Grizedale, forest red deer, 159, 160,
    161, 162, 163
growing season, definition, 80–81
growth, 57–8
  effect of density, 124
  habitat, 59
  nutrition, 59, 188
habitat, 7
  effect on body size, 2, 13, 59
  improvement for deer, 103
  major vegetation divisions, 79
heather, 7, 79, 80, 83, 85, 88, 89, 91,
    92, 94, 95, 99, 103, 135, 139,
    164, 167, 171, 173
  effect of production on deer
      density, 27, 28
  estimates of production, 229
  quality and muirburn, 96, 97
herring gull, 89
Highlands
  definition, 1

vegetation, 79, 85
Hill Farming Research Organisation
    (Glen Saugh), 79
home range, 45, 47
    in commercial forests, 166
    winter variation between sexes, 93
horsefly, *see* cleg
human influence on habitat, 13, 14
hybridisation of red & sika deer,
    173–4, 177
Hydropotes spp., 11

Invercauld, 14, 15
Invermark, 141, 144
Islay, 31

Juncus spp., 91
Jura, 29, 97, 177

key factor analysis, 121–22
kidney fat condition index, 65, 69

lactation
    cost of, 67, 103
    daily milk yields, 67
    suckling rate, 67
Laminaria spp., 87
Lagopus lagopus scoticus, 7
larch, 159
Larix spp., 159
Ledgowan, 32
leptospirosis, 101
Lepus timidus, 7
liver fluke, 101
lodgepole pine, 159, 167
lung worm, 101

management
    population dynamics, 192–200
    to increase growth, 103
    to reduce calf mortality, 103
    relationship with research, 200–205
management decision making,
    200–205
Mar, 14, 15
matrilineal groups, 45
    population stability, 186
matriline size
    calf mortality, 186
    fecundity, 186
    reproductive success, 45
maximum sustainable yield, 126–8
    of absolute numbers, 126–7, 153

difficulty in cull estimation, 128
    of venison, 127–8
milk hinds
    birth weight of offspring, 68
    body weight and condition, 67
    conception date, 67–8
    fecundity, 67
    food requirements, 67
    mortality, 67
metabolic rate, 133
milk yield
    daily, 67
    reproductive success of offspring,
        152
mixed stocking, productivity,
    99–100, 103–104
Molinia caerulea, see purple moor
    grass
mortality
    climatic correlates, 134–5
    effect of density, 118–23
    culling, 152
    neonatal, 119, 186
mortality, adult
    climate, 147–9
    density, 120
    of hinds, 67
mortality, calf, 118–21
    effect of birth weight, 56, 124, 150,
        186
    effect of conception/birth date, 57,
        177, 185
    effect of density, 117, 119, 120,
        121, 187
    effect of matrilineal group size, 186
    in forests, 163
    importance for population level,
        120–21
    mother's age, 65, 67
    mother's cohort, 150, 187
    to previously yeld hinds, 68–9, 70
    sex differences, 57, 121, 119, 187
    sexual dimorphism, 120
    summer, effect of climate, 142–3
    winter, effect of climate, 143–7
    winter, standing vegetation crop,
        147
mortality rate
    definition, 118
    effect of age, 64, 67
Morvern, 31
mountain hare, 7
muirburn, 96–7

deer management, 193
effect on reproductive success, 97
practice, 96
purpose, 96
mismanagement, 96
short-term effects, 96
Mull, 31, 32

Nardus stricta, 101
Nature Conservancy (Council), 97, 197
accuracy of counts, 210–14
systematic counts, 16, 26, 210, 211, 212
Norway Spruce, 159, 164
bark stripping, 169
browsing susceptibility, 167

overgrazing, 191

parasites and disease
influence of sheep, 101
parish-year model, 219
pellet counts, density estimation, 165
Picea abies, *see* Norway spruce
Picea sitchensis, *see* Sitka spruce
Pinus contorta, 159, 167
Pinus sylvestris, 159, 167
Poa spp., 94
population of red deer
in commercial forests, 159
counts in forests, 159–60
total in Highlands, 1, 25–6
population dynamics, current knowledge, 185–92
population stability
climate, 191–2
culling, 190–91
Populus tremula, *see* aspen
pneumonia, 101
purple moor grass, 79, 87, 88, 91, 93, 96, 99, 101, 103, 201

radio tracking, use in forests, 165
rainfall
calf mortality, 143, 144, 145, 147, 187
effect on vegetation, 79, 81, 82–3
fecundity, 139, 187
hind weight, 138–9
Rannoch, 31
raven, 201
recruitment, 37

culling level, 194–7
effect of population density, 112–29, 191
implications for management, 39
red deer, historical occurrence in Scotland, 13
Red Deer Commission, *see also* counts
counts, 2, 17, 26, 210
establishment of, 16, 190
marking programme and dispersal, 49, 189
membership, 17
statutory duties and activities, 16, 17
red grouse, 7
reindeer, 185, 191
reproduction, hinds
gestation, 54, 67
onset of estrus, 51, 52
synchrony of conception, 51–3, 54
yeld hinds, 53
reproduction, stags
onset of rut, 50
fighting success, 50
reproductive cycle, 53
reproductive success, 149–57
birth weight, 147, 149–52
climatic correlates, 134–5
culling, 199–200
cohort effects, 149–52, 187
effect of age, 63–7, 70
effect of climate at birth, 149–52
effect of dominance, 45
effect of forestry, 102
effect of muirburn, 97
effect of weight, 59, 149–52
matrilineal group size, 45
Rhum, 185, 186
altitude and terrain, 5
area, 23
climate
birth weight, 141, 142
conception timing, 140
fecundity, 139, 140
conception date distribution, 54, 140
condition of hinds, 69
conservation of 'pure' red deer, 177
counts, 23, 210
culling, 5, 45, 114, 152, 195–6, 197–8
density, 5, 29

antler size, 126
  changes, 115
  conception date, 117, 119
  conception threshold weight, 117
  dispersal, 124
  fecundity, 115, 116
dispersal of males, 71
diurnal feeding pattern, 83
diet, 79
  composition and variation, 85,
    87, 92, 94
  influence of weather, 92
  preferences, 88, 89, 90, 91
effect of cattle, 101
fecundity
  climate, 139, 140
  of yeld hinds, 67
growing season, 81
habitat use, 79
home ranges, 45, 93, 166
maximum sustainable yield, 126
mortality
  age-specific, 64, 67
  calf, 68, 121, 143
  climate, 143−5, 147, 148−9
  effect of density, 119, 121
  effect of mother's age on calf
    mortality, 65, 67
  neonatal, 119
muirburn, 96, 97
removal of sheep, 94, 100
standing live grass crop
  (September), 82
supplementary feeding, 98−9
weight
  birth weight, 123, 124
  effect of mother's age on birth
    weight, 65
  effect of winter temperature, 61,
    138
  hind weights, 139
  larder weights, 137, 161
  reproductive success, 149−50,
    152
roe deer, 159, 164, 172−3
  competition with red deer, 173
  diet, 164, 173
  distribution in Britain, 172
  forest habitat use, 173
Rosehall, 173
rowan, 171
Rowett Research Institute, 79
rump fat condition index, 69

Salix spp., see willow
Scarba, 116, 117
Schoenus sp., 103
Scots pine, 159, 167
seaweed in diet, 85, 92
Serengeti, 202
sex ratio at birth, in forests, 163
sex ratio, adult
  density, 187
  sexual dimorphism, 188
sexual dimorphism, sex ratio, 188
sheep
  deer stalking, 15, 16
  diet, 99−101
  effect on deer density, 29, 33, 38,
    100−101
  effects on vegetation, 94−5
  Highland Clearances, 14
  historical effects on deer, 14
  transmission of deer
    parasites/diseases, 101
  wintering, 7, 8
sheep population
  geographical density variations,
    8
  sympatric with red deer, 7
  changes in Highlands, 27, 28
Sheildaig, 32
shelter, 38, 90
  effect on digestion, 90−91, 103
  heat loss, 133, 140, 147, 152, 193
shelter belts, 103, 152
sika deer, 172, 173−4
  competition with red deer, 173
  control, 177
  distribution in Britain, 175
  hybridization with red deer, 173−4,
    177
silver fir, 171
  bark stripping, 169
Sitka spruce, 159, 164
  bark stripping, 169
  browsing susceptibility, 167
snow lie duration, 27, 28, 34
  adult mortality, 147−8
  antler shedding, 137, 138
  body weight, 137, 138
  calf mortality, 142−5
  mortality, 147−8
social behaviour, 44−54, see also
    dispersal and home range
  importance of older hinds, 70
  stability of male groups, 47

soil type
    effect on deer density, 33
    effect on vegetation, 79
stalking, 7
    close season, 16
    historical development, 15, 16
    local economy, 7, 8
suckling rate, 67, 68
supplementary feeding
    tree damage prevention, 171
    in winter, 97−9

tapeworms, 101
temperature
    effect on birth weight, 141, 142,
        187
    effect on plant growth, 80−81, 83
testosterone, 50
ticks, 101
tree regeneration, effect of browsing,
    96, 104, 169
Trichophorum cespitosum, see deer
    sedge
twinning, in forests, 161−3

Upper Mar, 147

Vaccinium spp., 171
Vaccinium myrtillus, see blaeberry
Vaccinium vitis-idaea, 171
voles, 163

wapiti, 13
weight, *see also* birth weight

in commercial forests, 161
    effect of climate, 135−9
    geographical variation, 59, 60, 61
    reproductive success 149−52
weight of calves
    population density, effect on
        mortality, 124
weight of females
    birth weight of offspring, 68
    effect of age, 65
    effect of altitude, 62
    effect of rainfall, 138−9
    fecundity, 116−17, 118
weight of males
    effect of snow cover, 137, 138
    effect of winter temperature, 138
    seasonal changes in stags, 48, 49
weight, conception threshold, 116,
    161, 185
willow, 171
    browsing susceptibility, 167
yeld hinds
    conception date, 67−8
    calf birth weights, 68, 70
    calf mortality, 68−9, 70
    condition, 67, 69
    culling of, 70
    definition, 53
    fecundity, 67
    survival, 67
    winter weight loss, 67, 69
weather, *see also* climate
    at birth and subsequent
        reproductive success, 149−52

Author Index

Italics refer to reference number.

Ahlen, I., 180(*21*)
Albon, S. D., 42(*4*), 75(*26*),(*27*),
    108(*30*), 130(*8*),(*9*),(*15*), 156(*12*),
    (*16*),(*19*),(*23*), 206(*2*),(*3*), 232(*4*)
Alexander, T.L., 111(*77*)
Alvey, N., 225(*1*), 247(*7*)
Anderson, J. E. M., 7(*58*)
Andrewartha, H. G., 155(*1*)
Appleby, M. C., 74(*5*)
Arman, P., 77(*57*)

Badenoch, C. O., 181(*32*)
Ball, D. F., 109(*49*)
Ball, M. E., 109(*52*)
Batchelor, L. L., 182(*66*)
Beddington, J. R., 156(*21*),
    209(*39*),(*40*),(*41*)
Bell, R. H. V., 209(*47*)
Beninde, J., 20(*34*)
Birse, E. L., 246(*2*),(*3*)
Blaxter, K. L., 20(*28*), 75(*2*), 107(*19*)
Bobek, B., 180(*29*)
Boyd, R. J., 108(*33*)
Brockway, J. M., 111(*74*)
Bryden, J. M., 20(*30*)
Bubenik, A. B., 182(*63*)
Bunce, R. G. H., 111(*82*), 246(*1*)

Cameron, A. G., 111(*78*)
Catt, D. C., 179(*8*), 208(*19*)
Caughley, G., 131(*23*), 207(*9*),
    208(*29*),(*32*),(*33*), 309(*43*),(*49*),
    215(*1*)
Chard, J. S. R., 180(*31*)
Charles, W. N., 107(*14*), 108(*32*)
Clutton-Brock, T. H., 18(*3*), 74(*2*),
    (*3*),(*4*),(*11*), 75(*12*),(*14*),(*25*),
    76(*28*), 77(*56*), (*59*),(*60*), 107(*16*),
    (*17*), 109(*46*), 130(*3*),(*4*),(*12*),(*13*),
    (*16*), 156(*15*),(*22*),(*24*), 180(*17*),
    107(*4*),(*6*),(*7*),(*8*),(*10*),(*12*),
    226(*4*), 231(*1*)
Colquhoun, I. R., 20(*25*), 107(*10*)
Corbet, G. B., 20(*37*)
Craig, J. F., 156(*25*)

Darling, F. F., 18(*1*), 77(*44*), 107(*24*),
    131(*21*)

Dasman, W., 209(*48*)
Deinum, B., 156(*12*)
Delpech, F., 20(*38*)
Douglas, M. J. W., 180(*22*)
Dunn, A. M., 111(*76*)
Dunnet, S. C., 110(*70*)
Dzieciolowski, R., 108(*34*), 180(*28*)

Easie, J., 20(*28*)
Ehrlich, H., 182(*55*)
Eiberle, K., 180(*26*)
Eick, E., 183(*71*)
Ellerman, J. R., 20(*36*)
Evans, H., 18(*5*), 21(*46*), 110(*68*)
Eygenraam, J. A., 108(*35*)

Fanta, B., 182(*59*)
Flerov, K. K., 20(*33*)
Fletcher, T. J., 75(*19*)
Fordham, R. H., 207(*14*)
Fowler, C. L., 206(*1*)
Fowler, C. W., 129(*2*)
Futty, D. W., 42(*10*), 247(*4*)

Galindo, C., 207(*16*)
Georgii, Von B., 207(*17*),(*18*)
Gibb, J. A., 108(*37*)
Gimingham, C. H., 107(*25*), 109(*53*),
    110(*63*)
Gloyne, R. W., 108(*28*)
Gordon, I., 107(*18*), 111(*80*)
Gordon-Duff-Pennington, P. T., 42(*9*)
Grace, J., 19(*15*), 109(*42*),(*44*), 155(*9*)
Grant, S. A., 109(*51*), 57
Greenwood, P., 74(*7*), 208(*20*)
Guinness, F. E., 75(*20*), 76(*29*)

Haaften, J. L., 182(*61*)
Habeehr, J. R., 182(*49*)
Hansen, L. P., 207(*15*)
Harper, J. A., 108(*32*)
Harrington, R., 183(*76*),(*77*),(*78*)
Hart-Davies, D., 20(*41*)
Hewson, R., 19(*16*), 106(*3*)
Hinge, M., 179(*9*)
Hobbs, R. J., 109(*50*)
Hobson, P. N., 109(*43*)
Hodgson, J., 109(*48*)

Hofmann, P. R., 183(*73*)
Holloway, C. W., 110(*60*), 180(*23*),(*25*)
Houston, D. B., 131(*19*), 182(*51*), 208(*34*)
Huxley, J. B., 20(*39*),(*40*), 77(*43*)

Iason, G. R., 75(*17*), 108(*39*), 208(*21*)
Illius, A. W., 207(*13*)

Jackes, A. D., 107(*11*)
Jacquest, S., 225(*2*)
Jarvis, E., 20(*31*)
Jeffrey, W. G., 179(*6*)
Jenkins, D., 182(*56*)
Jenson, P. V., 108(*36*)
Jewell, P. A., 208(*75*)

Kay, R. N. B., 20(*29*), 107(*20*),(*22*), 111(*75*)
Kiddie, D. G., 183(*75*)
Kinnaird, J. W., 110(*59*)
Klein, D. R., 208(*31*)
König, E., 182(*62*)
Krugge, W., 181(*44*)
Kurth, A., 181(*48*)

Lack, D., 155(*2*), 209(*50*)
Leader-Williams, N., 208(*27*)
Lincoln, G. A., 74(*9*),(*10*), 75(*13*), 77(*47*),(*48*),(*49*),(*50*),(*51*),(*52*), 215(*4*)
Lister, A. M., 20(*35*)
Locke, G. M. L., 179(*1*)
Logan, P. C., 183(*74*)
Loudon, A. S. I., 76(*39*), 182(*65*)
Lowe, V. P. W., 19(*11*),(*12*), 76(*33*), 77(*55*), 107(*13*), 110(*67*), 182(*68*),(*69*), 209(*44*),(*45*), 215(*5*),(*6*)

McComb, K., 75(*18*)
McIntyre, E. B., 181(*40*)
McNab, J., 131(*24*), 209(*42*)
McNeil, R. J., 182(*50*)
McVean, D. N., 107(*23*), 109(*47*)
Maloiy, G. M. O., 110(*72*)
Mann, J. C. E., 183(*72*)
Mathews, M. O., 109(*45*)
Maxwell, H. A., 181(*45*)
Miles, J., 109(*56*), 110(*64*)
Milne, J. A., 108(*40*), 110(*73*)
Miller, G. R., 108(*31*), 110(*58*),(*62*), 232(*2*)

Mitchell, B., 18(*2*),(*6*), 19(*13*), (*18*),(*22*), 20(*23*),(*26*), 74(*1*),(*8*), 75(*15*), 76(*31*),(*32*),(*34*),(*35*), 77(*45*),(*53*),(*54*), 106(*8*), 130(*6*), (*10*),(*14*), 131(*22*), 155(*4*),(*5*), 156(*13*), 179(*10*),(*11*), 180(*16*), 215(*8*)
Monthly Weather Records, 155(*8*)
Morris, R., 225(*3*)
Moss, R., 19(*17*), 106(*5*)
Muller, H. J., 181(*37*)
Mutch, W. E. S., 19(*14*), 77(*61*), 110(*71*)

Nahlik, A. J. de., 182(*60*)
Nannestad, L., 181(*46*)
Nethersole-Thompson, D., 21(*42*)
Nicholson, I. A., 110(*65*), 111(*79*)
Norton-Griffiths, M., 215(*2*)

Osborne, B. C., 19(*10*), 77(*62*), 107(*12*)

Paslawski, T., 182(*57*)
Peart, J. N., 111(*81*)
Pellew, R. A., 181(*41*)
Pemberton, J., 76(*30*)
Petrie, S. M., 180(*18*)
Pepper, A. W., 182(*58*)
Picton, H. D., 155(*7*), 209(*37*)
Podoler, H., 131(*18*)

Racey, P. A., 75(*21*)
Ratcliffe, P. R. 19(*7*),(*8*),(*9*), 42(*3*), 76(*36*),(*37*),(*38*), 179(*2*),(*4*), (*5*),(*12*),(*14*),(*15*), 182(*67*), 183(*79*),(*80*),(*81*)
Red Deer Commission, 110(*66*), 209(*46*)
    Annual reports: 1959−60, 129(*1*)
                    1961−83, 18(*4*)
                    1970, 42(*5*)
                    1976, 42(*6*)
                    1981, 41(*7*)
                    1983, 74(*6*)
                    1986, 42(*9*)
Reijnders, P. J. H., 181(*35*)
Rijcken, P. H. P., 181(*42*)

Sablina, T. B., 180(*27*)
Sauer, J. R., 156(*20*), 208(*36*)
Savory, L. J., 106(*7*)
Schubeler, W., 183(*70*)

Scrope, W., 21(*45*)
Simpson, A., 155(*10*)
Sinclair, A. R. E., 208(*23*),(*25*)
Skogland, T., 207(*5*), 208(*28*)
Sobanskii, G. G., 155(*6*), 209(*38*)
Staines, B. W., 19(*20*),(*21*), 20(*24*),
　　75(*23*), 179(*7*),(*13*), 106(*1*),(*2*),
　　107(*9*),(*15*), 108(*41*), 130(*71*),
　　180(*19*), 215(*7*), 232(*3*)
Stenin, G., 181(*36*)
Steven, H. M., 182(*54*)
Stewart, L. K., 41(*2*), 42(*7*)
Stickles, A., 181(*33*)
Strandgaard, H., 181(*39*)
Stubbe, C., 181(*34*)
Suttie, J. M., 76(*40*), 107(*21*)
Szederjei, A., 181(*43*)

Taber, R. D., 131(*20*), 208(*35*)
Thirgood, S. J., 180(*20*)

Thorne, E. T., 75(*24*), 156(*17*)

Ueckermann, E., 180(*30*), 181(*38*)

Varley, G. C., 130(*17*)
Veen, H. E., van de, 182(*64*)
Vrublovski, K. I., 182(*52*)

Walker, A. D., 42(*12*), 247(*6*)
Watson, A., 19(*19*), 21(*43*),(*44*),
　　106(*4*), 155(*3*),(*11*)
Watts, A., 76(*42*)
Welch, D., 106(*6*), 107(*26*),(*27*)
Western, D., 215(*31*)
Westhoff, V., 182(*53*)
Whitehead, G. K., 20(*32*), 21(*47*),
　　76(*41*)
Wiersema, G. J., 100(*69*)

Zaruba, C., 181(*47*)